Introduction

This is the second of two textbooks covering Intermediate Tier GCSE. Students following a two year course would expect to take one year on each book, those on a one year course half that time. The books cover the requirements of Intermediate Tier GCSE and so are suitable for use with any syllabus. The division of material between them is made on the basis of the modules within the MEI syllabus. This book also covers the mathematics requirements of GNVQ Application of Number at Level 3.

The book is divided into 16 chapters, forming a logical progression through the material (some teachers may however wish to vary this order). Each chapter is divided into a number of double-page spreads, designed to be teaching units. The material to be taught is covered on the left-hand page; the right-hand pages consist entirely of work for the students to do. Each chapter ends with a mixed exercise covering all of its content. Further exercise sheets and tests are provided in the Teacher's Resource.

The instruction (i.e. left-hand) pages have been designed to help teachers engage their students in whole class discussion. The symbol ⟨?⟩ is used to indicate a Discussion Point; teachers should see it as an invitation.

Most of the right-hand pages end with a practical activity. These are suitable for both GCSE and GNVQ students; some can be used for portfolio tasks. Advice on these is available in the Teacher's Resource and, where relevant, raw data is also supplied. Most students will not do all of the activities (they can be quite time-consuming) but the authors think it is important that they do as many of them as possible; they connect the mathematics classroom to the outside world and to other subjects.

Where knowledge is assumed, this is stated at the start of the chapter. There is a general expectation that students will know the content of Foundation Tier GCSE. Questions indicated with a calculator icon ▦ need to be answered with a calculator. The 'no calculator' icon ✕ indicates that a calculator should definitely not be used.

Although students are to be encouraged to use I.T., particularly spreadsheets, specific guidance is limited to the Teacher's Resource. Otherwise, the book would have been based on one particular package to the frustration of those using all the others.

The authors would like to thank all those who helped in preparing this book, particularly Chris Curtis for his advice on early versions of the manuscript, and Karen Eccles who has typed many a page.

Contents

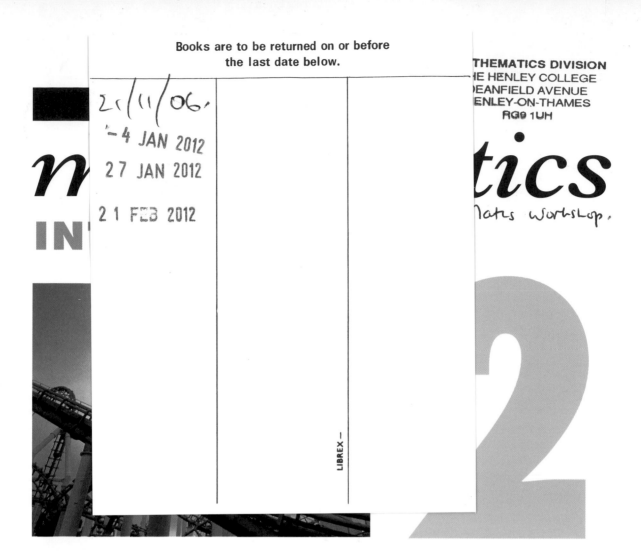

THEMATICS DIVISION
HE HENLEY COLLEGE
DEANFIELD AVENUE
ENLEY-ON-THAMES
RG9 1UH

m... *...tics*

INT...

...ates worbsLop.

2

Series editor: **Roger Porkess**

MEI author team:
Catherine Berry
Pat Bryden
Diana Cowey
Dave Faulkner
Julian Thomas
Christine Wood

Hodder & Stoughton

A MEMBER OF THE HODDER HEADLINE GROUP

Acknowledgements

The authors and publishers would like to thank the following companies, agencies and individuals who have given permission to reproduce copyright material. Every effort has been made to trace and acknowledge ownership of copyright. The publishers will be glad to make suitable arrangements with any copyright holder whom it has not been possible to contact.

Illustrations were drawn by Maggie Brand, Tom Cross, Bill Donohoe and Mark Walker of Ian Foulis and Associates.

Photo supplied by the Health Education Authority (page 90).

Page design and cover design by Lynda King.

Orders: please contact Bookpoint Ltd, 39 Milton Park, Abingdon, Oxon OX 14 4TD.
Telephone: (44) 01235 400414, Fax: (44) 01235 400454. Lines are open from 9.00 – 6.00, Monday to Saturday, with a 24 hour message answering service. Email address: orders@bookpoint.co.uk

British Library Cataloguing in Publication Data

A catalogue record of this title is available from The British Library

ISBN 0 340 705515

First published 1998

Impression number	10 9 8 7 6 5 4 3 2 1
Year	2004 2003 2002 2001 2000 1999 1998

Cover photo from Photonica.

Typeset by Multiplex Techniques Limited, Orpington, Kent.

Printed in Great Britain for Hodder & Stoughton Educational, a division of Hodder Headline Plc, 338 Euston Road, London NW1 3BH by Scotprint Ltd, Musselburgh, Scotland.

Contents

How to use this book

 This symbol next to a question means you need to use your calculator.

 This symbol next to a question means you are not allowed to use your calculator.

 This symbol means you will need to think carefully about a point and may want to discuss it.

Triangles

An **equilateral** triangle has 3 equal sides.

An **isosceles** triangle has 2 equal sides.

A **scalene** triangle has no equal sides.

A **right-angled** triangle has 1 right angle.

An **acuted-angled** triangle has 3 acute angles.

An **obtuse-angled** triangle has 1 obtuse angle.

$$\text{Area of a triangle} = \frac{1}{2} \times \text{base} \times \text{height}$$

Quadrilaterals

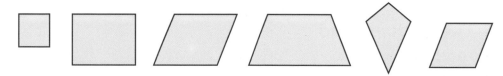

square   rectangle   parallelogram   trapezium   kite   rhombus

Area of a parallelogram = base $\times$ vertical height

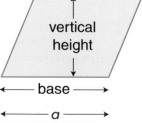

vertical height

base

$$\text{Area of a trapezium} = \frac{1}{2}\,(a + b)\,h$$

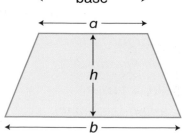

a

h

b

Circles

Circumference of circle $= \pi \times$ diameter

$\qquad\qquad\qquad\quad = 2 \times \pi \times$ radius

Area of circle $= \pi \times$ (radius)^2

Solid figures

Volume of cuboid = length $\times$ width $\times$ height

Volume of prism = area of cross section $\times$ length

Volume of cylinder = $\pi r^2 \times$ length

Trigonometry

$\sin \theta = \dfrac{\text{opposite}}{\text{hypotenuse}}$

$\cos \theta = \dfrac{\text{adjacent}}{\text{hypotenuse}}$

$\tan \theta = \dfrac{\text{opposite}}{\text{adjacent}}$

Pythagoras' rule: $x^2 + y^2 = h^2$

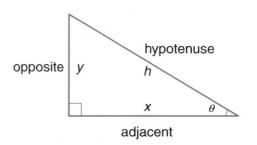

Units

Metric system

Length

k 1 kilometre $= 10^3$ metres $= 1000$ metres

h 1 hectometre $= 10^2$ metres $= 100$ metres

da 1 decametre $= 10^1$ metres $= 10$ metres

d 1 decimetre $= 10^{-1}$ metres $= \dfrac{1}{10}$ metre

c 1 centimetre $= 10^{-2}$ metres $= \dfrac{1}{100}$ metre : 100 centimetres $= 1$ metre

m 1 millimetre $= 10^{-3}$ metres $= \dfrac{1}{1000}$ metre : 1000 millimetres $= 1$ metre

The units for mass and capacity follow the same pattern. Notice that:

1 kilogram = 1000 grams   1 litre = 1000 millilitres

Notice also that: 1 tonne = 1000 kg

Imperial

12 inches = 1 foot   16 ounces = 1 pound

3 feet = 1 yard   14 pounds = 1 stone

1760 yards = 1 mile   8 stones = 1 hundredweight (cwt)

$\qquad\qquad\qquad\qquad\qquad$ 20 cwt = 1 ton

One

Fractions, decimals and percentages

> **Before you start this chapter you should be able to**
>
> ★ convert between improper fractions and mixed numbers
>
> ★ add and subtract fractions
>
> ★ do calculations involving decimals
>
> ★ find a fraction of a quantity
>
> ★ find a percentage of a quantity
>
> ★ compare using fractions, decimals or percentages.

Use the following questions to check that you still remember these topics.

Reminder

- $\frac{21}{8}$ is an **improper fraction** (or top heavy fraction)

- $2\frac{5}{8}$ is a **mixed number**

1 A sports hall is open 16 hours a day. This pie chart shows today's bookings. What fraction of time is booked to each activity?

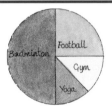

2 Change these improper fractions to mixed numbers.

a) $\frac{11}{4}$　　b) $\frac{13}{6}$　　c) $\frac{29}{8}$

d) $\frac{14}{3}$　　e) $\frac{22}{7}$　　f) $\frac{18}{5}$

3 Changes these mixed numbers into improper fractions.

a) $3\frac{1}{4}$　　b) $3\frac{7}{8}$　　c) $2\frac{7}{10}$

d) $5\frac{2}{3}$　　e) $7\frac{2}{5}$　　f) $4\frac{13}{16}$

4 Work out

a) $2\frac{7}{8} + \frac{5}{8}$　　b) $1\frac{3}{4} + 3\frac{3}{8}$　　c) $3\frac{7}{16} - 2\frac{1}{8}$　　d) $5\frac{1}{4} - 3\frac{11}{16}$

e) $2 - \frac{13}{16}$　　f) $4\frac{5}{8} + 1\frac{1}{2}$　　g) $4\frac{3}{4} - 1\frac{7}{8}$　　h) $1\frac{1}{2} + 2\frac{2}{3}$

i) $4\frac{7}{12} - 2\frac{1}{4}$　　j) $4\frac{2}{3} + 2\frac{5}{6}$　　k) $3\frac{7}{10} - 2\frac{1}{5}$　　l) $5\frac{3}{5} + 2\frac{1}{4}$

5 Arrange these numbers in order of size starting with the smallest.

a) $\dfrac{11}{20}, \dfrac{51}{100}, \dfrac{27}{50}, \dfrac{13}{25}$

b) $\sqrt{26}, 5.1, 5\dfrac{1}{5}, \dfrac{41}{8}$

6 Jodie is doing a survey for a video shop. She asks 80 people about the videos they like to watch. Three quarters like Horror films.

a) How many people is this?

b) Three quarters of the people who like Horror films watch more than one a month. How many people is this?

c) Two thirds of the people who like Horror films also like Action films. How many people is this?

7 Work out

a) $3.4 + 1.72$ b) $6.59 - 2.4$ c) 0.2×7 d) 4.8×5.1

e) 2.3×0.74 f) 0.65×10 g) $725 \div 10$ h) $6 \div 0.2$

i) $3.6 \div 0.08$ j) 4.2×0.25 k) 240×100 l) $8410 \div 100$

m) $0.17 \div 0.6$ n) 0.3×0.2 o) 3.12×0.05 p) 9.07×1000

8 Work out

a) 20% of 158   b) 7.5% of 600   c) 73% of £672.50

9 The management and union are discussing a pay rise.

Management offers 3.2%

UNION DEMANDS 4% Plus £20 per person

Robert earns £250 a week and Emily earns £300 a week.

a) How much extra does Robert earn if the union gets what it demands?

b) What percentage increase is this?

c) What is Emily's new wage if the management offer is accepted?

d) What is Emily's new wage if the union gets what it demands?

10 Philip and Samit are each doing a survey on smoking.
Philip finds 19 non-smokers out of 30 people questioned.
Samit finds 37 non-smokers out of 55 people questioned.
Compare their results.

Multiplying fractions

Dave, Becky and Ravi share a pizza.

 Dave has a quarter of it. How much is left?

Becky and Ravi share the other three quarters.

Each has half of it.

Each gets $\frac{1}{2}$ of $\frac{3}{4}$:

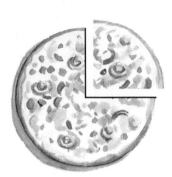

$$\frac{1}{2} \times \frac{3}{4} = \frac{3}{8}$$

> Multiply out:
> top $1 \times 3 = 3$
> bottom $2 \times 4 = 8$

 Dave only eats half of his piece. What is $\frac{1}{2} \times \frac{1}{4}$?

The pizza costs £8.00, but Ravi has a voucher for 30% discount.

Dave and Becky each work out how much this is.

> Dave multiplies first and then divides top and bottom by 100.

$$30\% \text{ of } 800$$
$$= \frac{30}{100} \times \frac{800}{1}$$
$$= \frac{24000}{100}$$
$$= 240$$

$$30\% \text{ of } 800$$
$$= \frac{30}{100} \times 800$$
$$= \frac{240}{1} \qquad = 240$$

> Becky divides top and bottom by 100 before multiplying. This is called **cancelling.**

 How much does Ravi pay for the pizza?

The next two examples show you how to multiply mixed numbers.

> Change $4\frac{1}{2}$ into an improper fraction

$$\frac{2}{3} \times 4\frac{1}{2}$$

> Cancel

$$= \frac{2}{13} \times \frac{9}{21}$$

$$= \frac{3}{1} = 3$$

> Multiply out and change back into a mixed number

$$2\frac{1}{3} \times 3\frac{3}{4}$$

> Change the mixed numbers into improper fractions

$$= \frac{7}{13} \times \frac{15}{4}$$

> Cancel

$$= \frac{35}{4}$$

$$= 8\frac{3}{4}$$

> Multiply out and change back to a mixed number

1 Work out

a) $\frac{1}{2} \times \frac{1}{3}$ b) $\frac{1}{2} \times \frac{3}{8}$ c) $\frac{1}{4} \times \frac{3}{5}$ d) $\frac{3}{4} \times \frac{5}{6}$

e) $\frac{3}{8} \times \frac{2}{3}$ f) $\frac{6}{7} \times \frac{7}{10}$ g) $\frac{3}{8} \times \frac{5}{8}$ h) $\frac{3}{4} \times \frac{10}{1}$

2 Work out

a) $\frac{1}{2}$ of 7   b) $\frac{3}{4}$ of 6   c) $\frac{1}{3}$ of 8   d) $\frac{2}{5}$ of 4

e) $\frac{5}{8}$ of 20   f) $\frac{2}{3}$ of 14   g) $\frac{3}{8}$ of 10   h) $\frac{5}{6}$ of 9

3 Work out

a) $\frac{1}{2} \times 6\frac{1}{2}$ b) $\frac{3}{4} \times 4\frac{1}{2}$ c) $\frac{1}{3} \times 2\frac{5}{8}$ d) $2\frac{1}{2} \times \frac{7}{10}$

e) $2\frac{4}{5} \times \frac{5}{8}$ f) $\frac{3}{4} \times 5\frac{1}{3}$ g) $1\frac{1}{2} \times 2\frac{1}{2}$ h) $2\frac{1}{4} \times 3\frac{1}{2}$

i) $3\frac{2}{3} \times 1\frac{1}{2}$ j) $5\frac{1}{3} \times 3\frac{3}{4}$ k) $1\frac{3}{8} \times 3\frac{1}{2}$ l) $6\frac{2}{5} \times 1\frac{7}{8}$

4 Amanda lives $2\frac{3}{4}$ miles from work. She works 5 days a week.
How many miles does she cover, travelling to and from work,
in a week?

5 (i)   (ii)

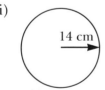

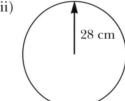

a) Using $\pi = 22/7$ find the circumference of each circle.

b) The radius of the second circle is twice the radius of the first.
What has happened to the circumference?

c) Using $\pi = 22/7$ find the area of each circle.

d) The radius of the second circle is twice the radius of the first.
What has happened to the area?

6 Paula buys 60 lbs of boiled sweets. She makes up twenty $\frac{1}{4}$ lb bags,
fifteen $\frac{1}{2}$ lb bags and fifteen $\frac{3}{4}$ lb bags.
How much has she left over?

Dividing fractions

Becky and Ravi share $\frac{3}{4}$ of a pizza.

$$\frac{1}{2} \text{ of } \frac{3}{4} = \frac{1}{2} \times \frac{3}{4} = \frac{3}{8}$$

They each have $\frac{3}{8}$ of the pizza.

Another way of working this out is to say $\frac{3}{4}$ of a pizza is divided between 2 people.

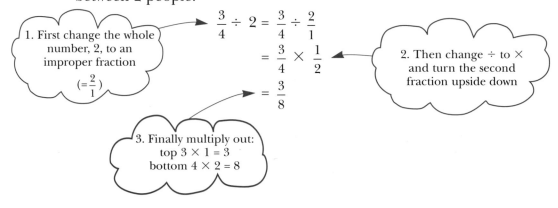

1. First change the whole number, 2, to an improper fraction $(=\frac{2}{1})$

$$\frac{3}{4} \div 2 = \frac{3}{4} \div \frac{2}{1}$$
$$= \frac{3}{4} \times \frac{1}{2}$$
$$= \frac{3}{8}$$

2. Then change ÷ to × and turn the second fraction upside down

3. Finally multiply out:
top $3 \times 1 = 3$
bottom $4 \times 2 = 8$

Dave, Becky and Ravi share $4\frac{1}{2}$ chocolate bars equally.

How much does each person get?

Ravi works it out like this: Dave does it like this:

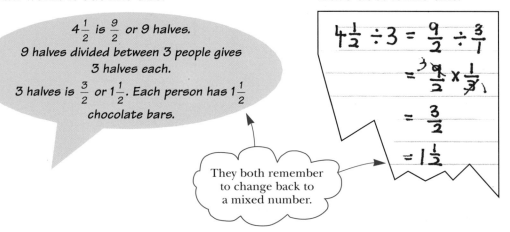

$4\frac{1}{2}$ is $\frac{9}{2}$ or 9 halves.
9 halves divided between 3 people gives 3 halves each.
3 halves is $\frac{3}{2}$ or $1\frac{1}{2}$. Each person has $1\frac{1}{2}$ chocolate bars.

$$4\frac{1}{2} \div 3 = \frac{9}{2} \div \frac{3}{1}$$
$$= \frac{\overset{3}{\cancel{9}}}{2} \times \frac{1}{\cancel{3}_1}$$
$$= \frac{3}{2}$$
$$= 1\frac{1}{2}$$

They both remember to change back to a mixed number.

Here are two more examples of division.

$$5 \div \frac{3}{4} = \frac{5}{1} \div \frac{3}{4}$$
$$= \frac{5}{1} \times \frac{4}{3}$$
$$= \frac{20}{3} = 6\frac{2}{3}$$

$$4\frac{1}{2} \div 1\frac{1}{4} = \frac{9}{2} \div \frac{5}{4}$$
$$= \frac{9}{1\cancel{2}} \times \frac{\cancel{4}^2}{5}$$
$$= \frac{18}{5} = 3\frac{3}{5}$$

1 Work out

a) $5 \div 4$ b) $\dfrac{1}{5} \div 2$ c) $1\dfrac{3}{5} \div 4$ d) $\dfrac{1}{3} \div 3$

e) $2\dfrac{1}{2} \div 5$ f) $2\dfrac{1}{4} \div 3$ g) $\dfrac{5}{8} \div 2$ h) $1\dfrac{1}{2} \div 6$

2 Work out

a) $4 \div \dfrac{1}{3}$ b) $3 \div \dfrac{1}{2}$ c) $12 \div \dfrac{3}{4}$ d) $12 \div \dfrac{2}{5}$

e) $3\dfrac{1}{2} \div 4$ f) $2\dfrac{1}{4} \div 1\dfrac{1}{4}$ g) $3\dfrac{3}{4} \div \dfrac{3}{8}$ h) $2\dfrac{3}{16} \div 1\dfrac{1}{4}$

i) $2\dfrac{5}{8} \div 3\dfrac{1}{2}$ j) $8\dfrac{3}{4} \div 1\dfrac{1}{4}$ k) $6\dfrac{7}{8} \div 2\dfrac{3}{4}$ l) $12 \div 3\dfrac{1}{3}$

3 A grocer buys pieces of cheese weighing 5 kg.

a) How many $\dfrac{1}{2}$ kg pieces can he get from this?

b) How many $\dfrac{1}{4}$ kg pieces can he get from it?

4 A box is $12\dfrac{1}{2}$ inches long, 5 inches wide and $1\dfrac{1}{4}$ inches high.

Toy bricks are cubes with edges $1\dfrac{1}{4}$ inches long.

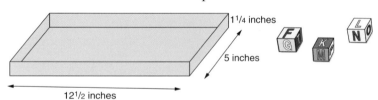

How many toy bricks can fit into the box?

5 Jermaine's car does 35 miles per gallon and he has 6 gallons of petrol in the tank.

How many times can he go to Fiona's house and back?

6 A bookshelf is $29\dfrac{1}{4}$ inches long.

How many books can fit on the shelf if each book is

a) $\dfrac{3}{4}$ inch thick?   b) $1\dfrac{1}{8}$ inches thick?   c) $1\dfrac{5}{8}$ inches thick?

Percentage problems

In mathematics you will often need to calculate a percentage of a quantity.

When you do these calculations you should make rough calculations to estimate the size of the answer you expect.

Alex has this carpet in the middle of her lounge.

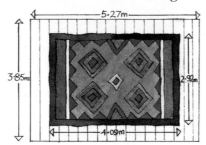

She estimates the percentage of floor left uncovered by the carpet.

First Alex estimates the area of the lounge.

Area of lounge (in m^2) = 5.27×3.85

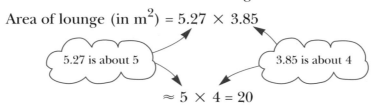

$\approx 5 \times 4 = 20$

Area of lounge is about 20 m^2.

Next Alex estimates the area of the carpet.

Area of carpet (in m^2) = 4.09×2.92

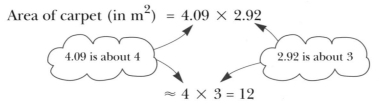

$\approx 4 \times 3 = 12$

Area of carpet is about 12 m^2.

Now Alex can estimate the area of floor uncovered.

$20\ m^2 - 12\ m^2 = 8\ m^2$

She uses these estimates to work out

percentage of floor uncovered = $\dfrac{\text{area of floor uncovered}}{\text{area of lounge}} \times 100$

$= \dfrac{8}{20} \times 100 = 40$

About 40% of the floor is left uncovered.

Work out, correct to one decimal place, the percentage of the floor area which is left uncovered by the carpet. How good is the estimate?

1 Ruth pays tax at 24p in the pound on her taxable income of £15 926.85.

a) Estimate how much tax she pays.
b) Work out, to the nearest penny, how much tax she pays.

Ruth's gross salary is £20 296.

c) Estimate the tax she pays as a percentage of her gross salary.
d) Work out, correct to one decimal place, the tax she pays as a percentage of her gross salary.

2 A group of holidaymakers are asked which activity they enjoy most. Their responses are shown here.

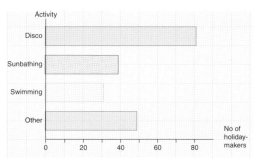

a) Estimate the number of responses.
b) What activity is chosen by about 40% of the respondents?
c) Estimate what percentage choose swimming.
d) Estimate what fraction of the holidaymakers choose 'other'.

3 Ella has an allotment. Her old plot is 40 feet by 30 feet. She takes a new plot where the sides are 20% longer.

a) What are the dimensions of the new plot?
b) What is the area of the new plot?
c) Work out the increase in area as a percentage of the area of the old plot.
d) Her old rent, based on area, is £25.92 a year. Estimate her new rent.

4 Charlotte's order is for £296.43.

a) Estimate how much discount she gets.
b) Work out exactly how much discount she gets.

Harry's order is for £1507.27.
He pays £1356.54.

c) Estimate how much discount he gets.
d) Estimate this discount as a percentage of the cost of the order.

☆☆BOOK WAREHOUSE☆☆
📖 CLOSING DOWN SALE📖

orders over £200
6% discount
☺☺☺☺☺☺☺☺☺☺☺☺☺
orders over £1000
ask about our special discount!

Further percentage problems

Josh works for a charity that wants to buy this computer.

The charity does not pay VAT.

He works out how much the charity pays like this:

Sonal's Store
£940 inc VAT

117.5% is 940

1% is $\dfrac{940}{117.5}$

100% is $\dfrac{940}{117.5} \times 100 = 800$

 How much does the charity pay for the computer?

Josh goes to another store and buys this printer. There is a special promotion today.

He pays £170 for the printer.

The usual price is 100% and the discount is 15% so he pays 100% − 15% = 85%

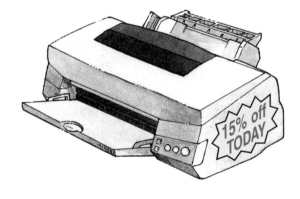

15% off TODAY

Josh works out the usual price like this:

85% is 170

1% is $\dfrac{170}{85}$

100% is $\dfrac{170}{85} \times 100 = 200$

 How much does Josh save by buying it on the special promotion?

1 These prices are inclusive of VAT at 17.5%.

Work out the price exclusive of VAT.

a)

£188

b)

£150

c)

£69.99

2 Jenna has just got a 4% pay rise. Her salary is now £13 000.

a) What was her salary before the rise?

b) Twelve months later she gets another 4% rise.

What is her salary after this rise?

3

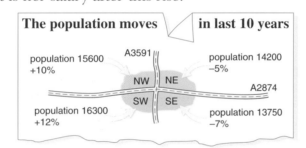

The newspaper gives the present population of each quarter of the town. The percentage change that has taken place in the last 10 years is also given.

a) What is the missing word in the headline? Choose North, South, East or West.

b) Work out the population of each quarter as it was 10 years ago.

c) Work out the percentage change in the number of people living North of the A2874.

4 Henry is a salesman. His sales are £350 000 this year.

This is 25% more than 3 years ago and 85% more than 7 years ago.

Work out his sales figures (to the nearest thousand pounds)

a) three years ago

b) seven years ago.

c) His target sales for next year is an 8% increase, with a further 8% increase the year after.

Work out his target sales figures for the next two years.

Repeated changes

Kelly works for Marina Drive car insurers.

She works out how much each driver has to pay, and then decides whether to give a discount by looking at this table.

MARINA DRIVE CAR INSURANCE

❶ Apply no claims discount
❷ Apply age discount
❸ Apply post-code discount

No claims	Age	Post-code
1 year 10%	17–20 none	AB51 10%
2 years 25%	21–25 5%	AB52 10%
3 years 40%	26–34 10%	AB53 5%
4 years 60%	35+ 20%	AB54 none

Stewart's car insurance premium is £800 before discount.

He has 2 years no claims, is 23 and lives in AB51.

How much no claims discount does he get?

£800 is reduced by 25% for no claims.

$$25\% \text{ of } 800 = \frac{25}{100} \times \frac{800}{1} = 200$$

After his no claims discount Stewart's insurance is

$$£800 - £200 = £600$$

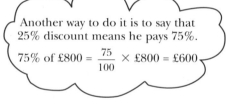

Another way to do it is to say that 25% discount means he pays 75%.

$$75\% \text{ of } £800 = \frac{75}{100} \times £800 = £600$$

How much age discount does he get?

£600 is reduced by 5% for age.

$$5\% \text{ of } 600 = \frac{5}{100} \times \frac{600}{1} = 30$$

After Stewart's age discount, his insurance is

$$£600 - £30 = £570$$

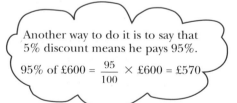

Another way to do it is to say that 5% discount means he pays 95%.

$$95\% \text{ of } £600 = \frac{95}{100} \times £600 = £570$$

How much post-code discount does he get?

How much does Stewart pay for his car insurance?

1 Use the table on the opposite page to work out the cost of car insurance for each of these people.

   a) Callum's insurance before discounts is £900.
      He has 4 years no claims, is 49 and lives in AB54.

   b) Nathan's insurance before discounts is £690.
      He has 1 years no claims, is 19 and lives in AB52.

   c) Dorothy's insurance before discounts is £750.
      She has 3 years no claims, is 34 and lives in AB53.

2 Russell and Kay run a fitness centre. Last year, 3250 people a month visited the centre.

Russell thinks these figures will increase by 5% this year and 9% next year.

Kay thinks there will be a 7% increase this year and another 7% increase next year.

   a) How many people does Russell expect next year?

   b) How many people does Kay expect next year?

3 Oliver sells 350 CDs in October. He expects sales will go up by a fifth in November and by a third in December.

   a) How many CDs does Oliver expect to sell in November?

   b) How many CDs does Oliver expect to sell in December?

4 Natasha buys a second hand car for £4000. She estimates that each year its value will fall by 20% of its value at the start of the year.

   a) How much is it worth after one year?

   b) How much is it worth after two years?

   c) What percentage decrease in value has taken place over 2 years?

5 Bob runs a travel company. He expects to increase prices by 5% next year.

   a) How much will the cruise cost next year?

   b) He expects to increase prices the following year by 4%.

      How much will the cruise cost the following year?

   c) How would the answer to b) be affected if the prices were increased by 4% next year and 5% the following year?

Mediterranean cruise

£1500

Finishing off

> **Now that you have finished this chapter you should be able to**
>
> ★ multiply and divide fractions
>
> ★ work out percentage problems when you don't know the original amount
>
> ★ do rough calculations to check your answer
>
> ★ work out repeated proportional changes.

Use the questions in the next exercise to check that you understand everything.

Mixed exercise

1 Work out

a) $2\frac{7}{8} + 1\frac{3}{4}$
b) $5\frac{1}{16} - 4\frac{1}{4}$
c) $5\frac{2}{3} - 1\frac{1}{6}$
d) $2\frac{4}{5} + 6\frac{7}{10}$

e) $\frac{1}{4} \times 2\frac{2}{3}$
f) $6\frac{3}{4} \times 1\frac{1}{2}$
g) $4\frac{5}{8} \times 1\frac{1}{4}$
h) $1\frac{1}{3} \times 3\frac{3}{4}$

i) $1\frac{1}{2} \div 2$
j) $2\frac{3}{4} \div \frac{1}{4}$
k) $1\frac{1}{8} \div 4\frac{1}{2}$
l) $6\frac{1}{4} \div 1\frac{2}{3}$

2 Work out

a) $5\frac{1}{2} - 3\frac{3}{4} - 1\frac{1}{8}$
b) $(\frac{2}{3} - \frac{1}{6}) \div 5$
c) $6 \div (\frac{1}{2} + \frac{1}{4})$

d) $2\frac{1}{2} \times 1\frac{3}{5} \times 1\frac{1}{4}$
e) $2\frac{1}{4} + 3\frac{2}{3} + 4\frac{1}{2}$
f) $(4\frac{1}{2} - 1\frac{1}{6}) \div \frac{3}{4}$

3 Work out

a) $4.2 + 3.97$
b) 0.3×0.3
c) $2 \div 0.4$
d) 1.65×2.4

e) $53.2 \div 10$
f) 39×100
g) 0.74×1000
h) $13.7 \div 1000$

4

a) Which television is the cheapest and how much does it cost?

b) The television in Geoff's Gadgets is inclusive of VAT at 17.5%. Work out the price exclusive of VAT.

5 Each day 4500 cars and 325 lorries cross this bridge.

a) How much is paid in tolls each day?

b) The car toll price is now increased by 30% and the lorry toll by 25%.

The number of cars crossing decreases by 5% and the number of lorries decreases by 8%.

How much is paid in tolls every day now?

BRIDGE TOLLS
£1 per car
£8 per lorry

6 At a rugby match two thirds of the crowd are home supporters, one quarter are away supporters and the remainder are neutrals.

There are 1250 neutrals. How large is the crowd?

7 Ranjit is looking at how prices have changed in the last 3 years.

Item	Price now	% change over last 3 years
House	£75 200	up 14%
Car	£11 400	up 11%
Computer	£1199	down 30%
Calculator	£7.50	down 25%

Work out the prices 3 years ago giving your answers to 3 significant figures.

8 Isabel is testing children's mental arithmetic skills using a 20 question test.

a) The pass mark is 16. What percentage is this?

Isabel tests children in 3 schools and gets these results.

b) Which school has the highest pass rate?

c) Which school has the lowest pass rate?

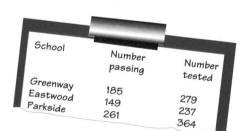

School	Number passing	Number tested
Greenway	185	279
Eastwood	149	237
Parkside	261	364

9 Jo sells 80 tennis rackets in May. She expects sales to increase by 20% in June and fall by a third in July. How many tennis rackets does she expect to sell in July?

Two

Formulae and equations

Before you start this chapter you should be able to

★ carry out calculations in the correct order

★ multiply and divide using negative numbers

★ add and subtract using negative numbers

★ understand the meanings of $2x$ and x^2

★ expand brackets

★ collect together like terms

★ solve simple equations

★ read information from a graph.

Use the following questions to check that you still remember these topics.

Reminder

• The correct order for a calculation is

   Brackets, Indices, Divide, Multiply, Add, Subtract (BIDMAS).

• When adding and subtracting with negative numbers a number line is helpful.

• When multiplying or dividing with negative numbers, or when there are two signs before a number,

   + with + gives +   + with − gives −   − with − gives +

• $2x$ means $2 \times x$ and x^2 means $x \times x$.

Always start by copying the expression in the question, then work down your page so you can see where each term comes from.

1 Simplify each of these, remembering to work in the correct order.

a) $6 + 3 \times 2$

b) $14 + 3 \times 3 - 2^3$

c) 2×3^2

d) $2(4x - 7)$ when $x = 3$

e) $2(x - 4)$ when $x = 4$

f) $5n^2$ when $n = 2$

g) $x \div 3$ when $x = 0$

h) $(2n)^2$ when $n = 5$

i) $(10 + 2)(5 - 5)$

j) $(x + 4)(x + 1)$ when $x = 3$

Revision exercise

2 Simplify these.

a) $2 - 12$ b) $5 + 13 - 20$ c) $-2 - 6 - 9$

d) $8x - 12x$ e) $4m + 2m - 5m$ f) $3c - 4c + c$

3 Write these as briefly as possible.

a) $3 \times a + 6 \times b$ b) $12 - 6 \times x$

c) $3 \times 5 \times c$ d) $3 \times n \times n \times n \times n$

4 Simplify these.

a) $5 \times (-3)$ b) $-2 \times (-2)$ c) $12 \div (-4)$ d) $-12 \div 4$

e) $6 + (-2)$ f) $8 - (-5)$ g) $3y \times (-2)$ h) $-4m \div (-2)$

5 Solve each of these equations to find the unknown.

a) $17 + x = 98$ b) $12x = 84$ c) $y - 46 = 23$

d) $5x + 12 = 99$ e) $34.8 - x = 25.8$ f) $2x + 7 = 0$

6 Expand these brackets.

a) $2(n - 3)$ b) $(a - b + c) \times 7$

c) $(5a + 6) \times 4$ d) $3(4y - 2z)$

7 Collect together the like terms and then simplify these expressions.

a) $2n + 3 + 3n - 4$ b) $6y - 5 + 10 - 6y$

8 Expand the brackets and then simplify these by collecting like terms.

a) $2(x + 8) + 1$ b) $12 + (5 + y)$

c) $3 + 2(2n - 1)$ d) $7 - 3(a - 2)$

9 These graphs have been drawn by using equations to work out the co-ordinates. One is $y = x$, one is $y = x^2$ and the other is $y = \dfrac{1}{x}$.

a) 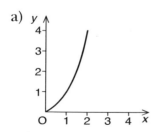   b) 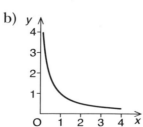   c)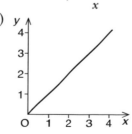

Which equation fits which graph? Give reasons for your answers.

Substituting into a formula

Tom is looking up how long it takes to roast a goose. His cookery book says 45 *minutes per kg plus 20 minutes.*

Tom's goose weighs 2.7 kg. For how long should he cook it?

Tom works it out like this:

cooking time (minutes) is
2·7 × 45 + 20
= 121·5 + 20
= 141·5
That's 2 hours 21½ minutes

You can use algebra to write the formula. Calling the weight of the goose *w* kg and the cooking time *t* minutes, the formula would be

$$t = 45w + 20$$

You just substitute for the weight of the goose.

Look carefully at this formula.

Where does the '45w' come from?

Where does the '+ 20' come from?

Example

Tom has another goose of weight 3.2kg.

Use the formula to work out the cooking time for this one.

Solution

Substituting $w = 3.2$ into the formula gives

$$t = 3.2 \times 45 + 20$$
$$= 144 \qquad + 20$$
$$= 164$$

The cooking time is 2 hours 44 minutes.

1 Calculate s in each of these formulae by substituting the numbers given.

a) $s = 4u + 80$ (i) $u = 2$ (ii) $u = 5$ (iii) $u = 6.5$

b) $s = 4u + 8a$ (i) $u = 2$, $a = 5$ (ii) $u = -6.5$, $a = 10$

2 The area, A, of a trapezium is given by

$$A = \frac{1}{2} h (a + b)$$

Find the value of A when

a) $a = 6$, $b = 4$, $h = 2$
b) $a = 16$, $b = 4$, $h = 5$
c) $a = 8$, $b = 8$, $h = 8$

3 The volume, v m^3, of gravel required for a rectangle of dimensions w metres by l metres is given by the formula

$$v = 0.05 lw$$

Find the volume required for

a) a path 1 m wide and 20 m long

b) a driveway 2.5 m wide and 12.5 m long

4 When a stone is dropped down a well, you can use the formula

$$d = 5t^2$$

to estimate its depth d in metres, where t is the time in seconds it takes to reach the bottom. Find d when $t = 4$.

5 Clare is making curtains. The length of fabric she needs for a window d metres deep is l metres, where

$$l = n(d + 0.5).$$

The number n depends on the width of the window.

How many metres of fabric must Clare buy when $n = 2$ and $d = 2.5$?

6 When a ball is thrown straight up in the air at 5 metres per second, its *upward* speed v metres per second after t seconds is given by the formula

$$v = 5 - 10t$$

Find v when t is:

a) 0   b) 0.2   c) 0.5   d) 1

Write down what is happening to the ball in each case.

You would use the formula for cooking a goose that is given on the opposite page, $t = 45w + 20$, if you had metric scales.

The rule usually used for a goose weighed in pounds is 'Twenty minutes plus twenty minutes per pound'. Write this as a formula.

Draw a graph with two lines on it, one for each formula. Cooking time should be on the vertical axis and the weight of the goose on the horizontal axis. The horizontal axis should be marked in both kilograms and pounds.

Working with unknowns

Try this out on a few people.

> *'Think of a number,......add 1,......multiply by 2,......add 4,*
> *......divide by 2,......subtract the number you first thought of,*
> *......what is your answer?'*

What happens? Why?

Justin uses algebra to work out what is happening.

Since he doesn't know what number a person will think of, he calls it *n*.

He writes this:

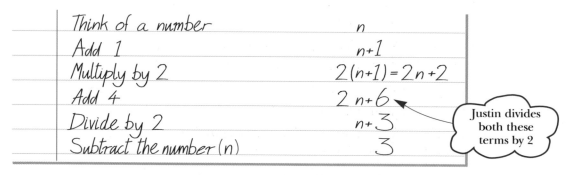

Think of a number	n
Add 1	$n+1$
Multiply by 2	$2(n+1) = 2n+2$
Add 4	$2n+6$
Divide by 2	$n+3$
Subtract the number (n)	3

Justin divides both these terms by 2

The answer is 3. It does not depend on the value of *n*. So whatever number the person thinks of, the answer will be 3.

This sets Justin thinking. He invents this new trick.

> *'Think of a number,......add 2,......multiply by 4,......add 2,*
> *......divide by 2,......subtract 5,......tell me the answer.'*

When people tell him the answer, Justin tells them the number they first thought of. He gets it right every time.

How does Justin know what number the person first thought of?

Find the rule that links the answer to the number you first thought of.

How can you use algebra to prove that your idea is right?

1 **This question revises the use of brackets. Check that you understand it before you go on to the other questions.**

Write these without brackets and simplify them where possible.

a) $4(n + 2)$ b) $5(m - 2)$ c) $7(4 + 2x)$

d) $8(2 - 3y)$ e) $3(2 - x) + 5$ f) $10(n + 4) - 30$

g) $2(3x + 6) - 12$ h) $15 + 3(x - 5)$ i) $5(5x + 2) - 16$

j) $10 - 2(n + 1)$ k) $22 - 3(a + 5)$ l) $4 - 2(x - 1)$

2 Work through these using n for the number. For each one say what answer you would expect.

a) *'Think of a number,......subtract 1,......add 4,......subtract the number you first thought of.'*

b) *'Think of a number,......add 2,......multiply by 2,......subtract 2, ...divide by 2,......subtract the number you first thought of.'*

c) *'Think of a number,......multiply by 10,......add 2,...... multiply by 3, ...subtract 6,......divide by the number you first thought of.'*

d) *'Think of a number,......subtract 1,......multiply by 5,......add 5, ...divide by the number you first thought of.'*

Check your answers by trying the tricks out on someone.

3 Try this with a few numbers:

'Think of a number,......add 10,......multiply by 10,......subtract 100.'

a) Describe how you can 'mind read' the number first thought of once you are told the answer.

b) Use algebra to show how this works.

4 Work through these as in question 3, then explain how to work out the original number. Try them out to check your answers.

a) *'Think of a number,......subtract 1,......multiply by 4,......add 8, ...divide by 4.'*

b) *'Think of a number,......add 3,...... multiply by 3,...... subtract 3, ...divide by 3.'*

c) *'Think of a number,......subtract 1,......multiply by 10,...... subtract 10, ... divide by 10.'*

Make up some 'Think of a number......' puzzles.
Check them through, using algebra, and make sure they don't involve any very difficult mental arithmetic.

Using equations to solve problems

 Which of these telephone companies is cheaper if you make just a few calls a month?

Which is cheaper if you make a lot of calls each month?

How do you decide which is cheaper for you?

You can do this using trial and error, or you can gain a clearer picture of the situation by using algebra.

The charges depend on the number of minutes that your calls last each month. Call the number of minutes m.

> It is important to be clear about what the letters and expressions stand for, and what units they are in.

The amount in pence charged by Venus is then $5m$.

The amount in pence charged by Connect is $1200 + 2m$.

 What does the 1200 represent in the expression for Connect's charges?

To find the value of m for which both companies charge the same amount, you form an equation and then solve it.

The companies charge the same amount when $\quad 5m = 1200 + 2m$

Subtract $2m$ from both sides $\qquad\qquad\qquad\quad 3m = 1200$

> This is an equation in m.

Divide both sides by 3 $\qquad\qquad\qquad\qquad\qquad\; m = 400$

....

The companies charge the same amount when $\quad m = 400$.

....

 Nick's calls last about 600 minutes each month. Which company should he use?

Catherine's calls are usually under 300 minutes each month. Which company should she use?

There are many situations in which forming and solving an equation is helpful.

 A chocolate bar is marked '25% extra free'. Its weight is 250 g.

How would you form an equation to find the weight of a normal bar?

1 **This question revises how to solve equations. Check that you understand it before you move on to the next questions.**

Solve these equations.

a) $2x + 5 = 25$　　　　b) $3x - 8 = 10$　　　　c) $4x - 9 = 2x + 11$

d) $x + 8 = -x + 14$　　e) $3x + 4 + x = 3x + 7$　　f) $5(x + 2) = 2x + 22$

g) $5(x + 4) = 4(x + 5) + 3$　　h) $7(x + 7) = 49$　　i) $3(x - 2) = 4x - 7$

2 For each of the following situations
(i)　form an equation in the unknown quantity given
(ii)　solve the equation
(iii)　check your answer.

a) Fanzia goes shopping with £100 in her purse. She buys x CDs at £12 each and still has £16 left.

b) In one season, Totnes Wanderers Football Club scores 72 points. They win w matches (3 points each), draw 6 (1 point each) and lose the rest (0 points).

c) The length of a field is 3 times its width of w metres. The perimeter is 600 m.

d) The largest angle of a triangle is 4 times the size of the smallest angle, $A°$. The third angle is 60°.

e) Halley's present age is y years. In 24 years time he will be 3 times as old as he is now.

3 Sara is finding out about monthly charges for using the Internet. She has written these notes.

Sara intends to surf the Internet for more than 5 hours. Suppose x stands for the number of extra hours (above 5) that she spends.

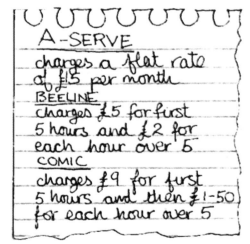

A-SERVE
charges a flat rate
of £15 per month
BEELINE
charges £5 for first
5 hours and £2 for
each hour over 5
COMIC
charges £9 for first
5 hours and then £1·50
for each hour over 5

a) Write down expressions for the amount Sara could expect to be charged by each company.

Which is cheapest when $x = 1$?
Which is cheapest when $x = 10$?

b) For a certain value of x, A-serve and Beeline must charge the same. Put those two expressions equal to each other, and solve the resulting equation to find this value of x.

c) Repeat b) to find a value of x for which Beeline and Comic charge the same.

d) Do the same for A-serve and Comic.

e) What advice would you give Sara?

Using graphs to solve equations

In many real-life problems you get equations that are too complicated to solve by algebra, but you still need to know the answer. You can find it by drawing a graph.

This graph shows the fuel consumption of a car (in miles per gallon) being driven at different speeds (in m.p.h.). The equation of the curve is

$$y = \frac{1}{10\ 000} (x^3 - 250x^2 + 15\ 000x + 200\ 000)$$

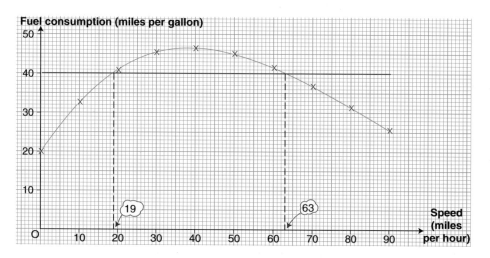

A car's fuel consumption is 40 miles per gallon. How fast is it travelling?

To find the answer you need to solve the equation

$$\frac{1}{10\ 000} (x^3 - 250x^2 + 15\ 000x + 200\ 000) = 40$$

You cannot solve this equation by algebra but you can do it by looking at the graph. The red line is $y = 40$ and this crosses the curve when x is about 19 or 63.

A graph only gives an approximate answer, but you can find one as accurately as you like by using Trial and Improvement. This method is used here to find a more accurate answer for the speed near 63 m.p.h.

When $x = 63$ $y = 40.27.....$ $\Big\}$ The answer is between 63 and 64. Try 63.5.
When $x = 64$ $y = 39.8....$

When $x = 63.5$ $y = 40.04$

When $x = 63.6$ $y = 40.002$ This is very close.

 Is 63.6 closer than 63.7? How can you find the answer even more accurately?

Formulae and equations

1 Jane is a scientist. She needs to solve the equation

$$x^2 - 6x + \frac{12}{x} = 0$$

So she draws the curve

$$y = x^2 - 6x + \frac{12}{x}$$

It is shown here. She is only interested in positive (+) values of x.

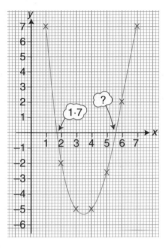

a) You can see from the graph that one of the values of x is near 1.7. Write down the other value, approximately.

b) Use Trial and Improvement to find the value of x near 1.7 to 2 decimal places.

c) Use Trial and Improvement to find the other value to 2 decimal places.

2 a) Copy and complete this table of values for $y = x^3 - 3x^2 - x + 3$.

x	–2	–1	0	1	2	3	4
x^3	–8						64
$-3x^2$	–12			–3			–48
$-x$	+2				–2		–4
+3	+3						+3
y	–15						+15

b) Draw the graph of $y = x^3 - 3x^2 - x + 3$.

c) Use your graph to solve the equations

   (i) $x^3 - 3x^2 - x + 3 = 0$

   (ii) $x^3 - 3x^2 - x + 3 = 8$

d) Use Trial and Improvement to find the value of x in c) part (ii) to 2 decimal places.

3 a) Make out a table of values for $y = \frac{20}{x} - 16 + x^2$ for $x = 1, 2, 3$ and 4.

b) Draw the graph.

c) Use your graph to solve $\frac{20}{x} - 16 + x^2 = 0$.

d) Use Trial and Improvement to find your answers to c) to 2 decimal places.

Changing the subject of a formula

Look at these two headlines
They both tell you the same thing.

Pele is the subject of the first.
The winning goal is the subject
of the second.

Look at this formula for finding the temperature, *F*, in degrees
Fahrenheit from the temperature, *C*, in degrees Celsius.

$$F = 1.8C + 32$$

The Fahrenheit temperature *F* is on its own on the left. It is the **subject**
of the formula. It is easy to find the value of *F* when you know the
value of *C*.

 Find the value of F when C is 20.

You probably found the formula very easy to use in this way. But what if
you know the value of *F* and you want to find *C*?

 Find the value of C when F is 77.

This would be easier with a formula for *C* in terms of *F*, in other words
to have *C* as the subject of the formula. You can make *C* the subject by
rearranging the formula as follows.

$$F = 1.8C + 32$$

Subtract 32 from both sides $\quad F - 32 = 1.8C$

Divide both sides by 1.8 $\quad \dfrac{F - 32}{1.8} = C$

or $\quad\quad\quad\quad\quad\quad\quad\quad\quad C = \dfrac{F - 32}{1.8}$

> Rearranging the formula is a bit
> like solving an equation. You
> want to get *C* by itself on one
> side, but at each step you have
> to do the same thing to each
> side of the formula

> This means the same as
> $(F - 32) \div 1.8$

You can see that *C* is now the subject of the formula.

You might have seen this formula in another form: $\quad C = \dfrac{5}{9}(F - 32)$.

 Find C when F is 59 *using both of these versions of the formula.*

Why do the two formulae give the same answer?

1 Make x the subject of each of these.

a) $y = x + 4$ b) $y = x + 20$ c) $y = x + a$

d) $y = 3 + x$ e) $y = 13 + x$ f) $y = c + x$

g) $y = x - 5$ h) $y = x - 11$ i) $y = x - b$

j) $y = 6 - x$ k) $y = 1 - x$ l) $y = d - x$

2 Make x the subject in each of these.

a) $y = 2x$ b) $y = 0.1x$ c) $y = ax$

d) $y = \dfrac{x}{4}$ e) $y = \dfrac{x}{10}$ f) $y = \dfrac{x}{b}$

g) $y = \dfrac{3}{4}x$ h) $y = \dfrac{5}{3}x$ i) $y = \dfrac{a}{b}x$

j) $y = \dfrac{4x}{5}$ k) $y = \dfrac{11x}{2}$ l) $y = \dfrac{ax}{b}$

3 Make t the subject of each of these.

a) $x = 2t - 3$ b) $y = 3t + 4$ c) $p = 6 + 2t$

d) $c = 4 - t$ e) $z = 6 - 2t$ f) $s = 2t + a$

g) $x = 5t - c$ h) $n = 7t - 3x$

4 In each of these, make the given letter the subject.

a) $v = u + at$, $\quad u$ b) $p = 2l + 2b$, $\quad l$

c) $V = 4x - 9y$, $\quad x$ d) $v = u + at$, $\quad t$

5 In each of these, expand the bracket and then make x the subject.

a) $p = 2(x + y)$ b) $V = 12(r + x)$

c) $s = 4(2 - x)$ d) $y = 4(a - x)$

6 In each of these, make the given letter the subject.

a) $A = lb$, $\quad l$ b) $V = lbh$, $\quad h$ c) $V = IR$, $\quad R$

d) $c = \pi d$, $\quad d$ e) $c = 2\pi r$, $\quad r$ f) $I = \dfrac{r}{100} \times P$, $\quad P$

g) $I = \dfrac{PRT}{100}$, $\quad T$ h) $I = \dfrac{PRT}{100}$, $\quad R$

All of the formulae in question 6 are real.

What do they refer to?

Write down six more formulae that you can use in mathematics or elsewhere.

Finishing off

> **Now that you have finished this chapter you should**
>
> ★ be able to substitute numbers into formulae
>
> ★ be confident about working with brackets
>
> ★ be able to use equations to solve problems
>
> ★ be able to change the subject of a formula.

Use the questions in the next exercise to check that you understand everything.

Mixed exercise

1 Write each of these expressions without brackets and then simplify it.

a) $3(x + 2)$

b) $5(x + 2) + 2(x + 3)$

c) $6 + 2(x - 3)$

d) $12(m + 5) - 34$

e) $21 + 3(x - 7)$

f) $13 - 4(n + 1)$

g) $21 - 5(x - 1)$

h) $6 - 3(2y - 1)$

i) $11 - 6(3x - 5)$

2 Alf has a decorating business and he can claim back the VAT that he spends on materials. When he spends £P the VAT is given by the formula

$$V = \frac{7}{47} \times P$$

Find the amount of VAT he can claim for paint costing £23.50.

3 Work out the time Mac should cook a turkey weighing 6.3 kg by:

a) using the rule *15 minutes per 450 g plus 15 minutes*;

b) using the formula $T = 33W + 15$ where T is the time in minutes for a turkey weighing W kg. Is your answer close enough to a)?

4 Tariq throws a snowball. At any point during its flight the snowball's height, y metres, is related to its horizontal distance, x metres, by the equation

$$y = x - \frac{1}{6}x^2 + \frac{1}{2}.$$

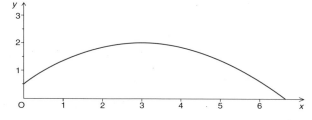

The graph of this equation is shown in the diagram.

a) Use the equation to find y when $x = 0$, 3 and 7.

b) What do your answers to a) tell you about the height of the snowball at each of these points?

c) Tariq is aiming to hit a fence 7 m away. Does he succeed?

5 Make x the subject of each of these.

a) $y = 3x + 4$ b) $y = ax$ c) $t = 7 - 2x$

d) $s = px + q$ e) $u = \frac{1}{2}rx$ f) $v = a - bx$

6 Sunny Days Travel requires a deposit of 10% when a holiday is booked.

This can be written as a formula for the deposit £d for a holiday for n people priced at £p per person:

$$d = \frac{np}{10}$$

a) Calculate d when $n = 4$ and $p = 150$.

b) Jack paid a deposit of £85 for 2 people.
   What was the price per person?

c) Make p the subject of the formula.

7 Ching asks Jo to think of a number, then to subtract 1, multiply by 4, and finally subtract 10.

a) Calling Jo's number n, find an expression for her answer in terms of n.

b) Jo says her answer is twice the number she first thought of.

   Make an equation for n and solve it to find Jo's number.

8 Morag buys a coat that has been reduced by 20%. The original price was £C.

a) Write 20% as a decimal, and so write an expression for the amount by which the coat was reduced, in terms of C.

b) Find the sale price of the coat in terms of C.

c) Morag actually paid £48 in the sale. Make an equation and solve it to find C.

9 When Grandma Jones visits her family, her return train fare is £15.

a) Write down an expression for the cost of x return journeys.

b) Grandma Jones could buy a railcard for £20. With the railcard the fare is reduced to $\frac{2}{3}$ of the usual price for a period of one year.
   Write an expression for the total cost of x journeys using the railcard.

c) Use your answers to a) and b) to find a value of x which will make the costs equal.

d) How many times a year does Grandma Jones need to visit her family to make it worth buying a railcard?

Three

Triangles and polygons

Before you start this chapter you should

* ★ be able to find the interior and exterior angles of any regular polygon

* ★ be able to find pairs of equal angles where two lines cross and where a line intersects parallel lines

* ★ be able to find the sum of the angles of any polygon

* ★ know that the angle sum of a triangle is 180° and the angle sum of a quadrilateral is 360°

* ★ know that angles round a point add up to 360° and angles on a straight line add up to 180°

* ★ be able to draw tessellations with simple shapes.

Use the following questions to check that you still remember these topics.

Reminder

* • Where two lines intersect, opposite angles are equal.

* • Where a line intersects with two parallel lines, corresponding angles are equal.

* • Where a line intersects with two parallel lines, alternate angles are equal.

Look for the letter F

Look for the letter Z

To find the angle sum of any polygon you split the polygon into triangles, or use the formula

Angle sum = (number of sides − 2) × 180°

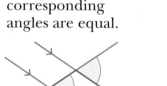

To find the interior angle of a regular polygon, you divide the angle sum by the number of sides.

To find the exterior angle of a regular polygon, you divide 360° by the number of sides.

1 Use squared paper to draw tessellations of these shapes.

a)

b)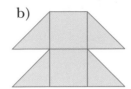

2 Find the angles marked with letters in these diagrams.

a)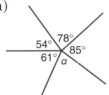

b)

c)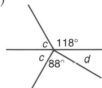

d)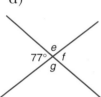

e)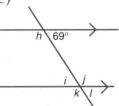

f)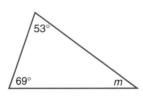

g)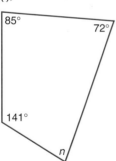

h)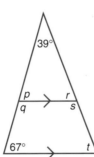

i)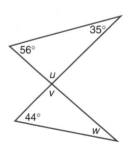

3 Find the angle sum of each of these polygons.

a)

b)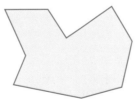

4 Find the interior angle and exterior angle of

a) a regular hexagon (6 sides)

b) a regular decagon (10 sides).

More about angles in polygons

Finding the number of sides of a polygon

Stuart is designing floor tiles. He wants to make the tiles in the shape of a regular polygon.

They need to fit together without a gap. In other words, they need to **tessellate**

Stuart would like a design in which three polygons fit together.

He works out that the interior angle of the polygon he needs must be 120°.

 How did he work this out?

Now Stuart needs to know what polygon has an interior angle of 120°.

 Stuart finds that his polygon has 6 sides. It is a hexagon.

How did Stuart work this out?

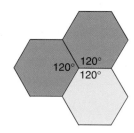

Finding out whether a shape tessellates

Stuart wonders if he can make floor tiles in the shape of a pentagon.

He puts three pentagons together round a point.

You can see that pentagons will not fit together without leaving gaps.

 What angle is the gap?

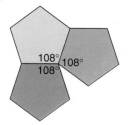

You can find out if any regular polygon tessellates by working out the size of its interior angle. Do they fit exactly round a point?

If the interior angle is a factor of 360°, the polygon will tessellate.

1 Work out the number of sides of a polygon with an interior angle of

a) 144°   b) 150°   c) 135°

2 Sophie wants to make a tessellation which has 6 regular polygons fitting round a point.

a) What must the interior angle of her polygon be?
b) How many sides does the polygon have?
c) Draw Sophie's tessellation.

3 a) Work out the interior angle of a regular 9-sided polygon.
b) Is it possible to make a tessellation of these polygons?

4 a) Explain why it is not possible to make a tessellation of regular octagons.

b) What angle is left over when you have fitted as many octagons as possible together?

c) What shape would fit in the gap?

Draw a repeating pattern using octagons and this other shape.

5 In this question you will discover a useful rule about angles which you should try to remember.

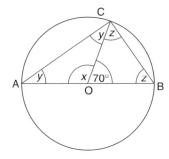

The diagram shows a circle, with centre O. AB is a diameter of the circle and C is a point on the circumference of the circle. OA, OB and OC are all radii of the circle, so the triangles OAC and OBC are both isosceles.

a) (i) Find the angles marked with letters.

(ii) Find the angle ACB by adding together angles y and z.

b) Choose a different angle instead of 70° for angle COB, and repeat part a) of this question. Do this several times.

c) What have you found out about the angle ACB?

6 Check that your answer to question 5 c) is correct before you start this question. You will need to use the rule that you have found.
In each of these diagrams, PQ is a diameter of the circle.
Find the angles a and b.

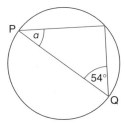

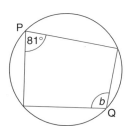

Pythagoras' rule

Robert is a farmer and is building a gate for one of his fields. He sketches out a rough design for the gate so that he can work out what lengths of wood he needs.

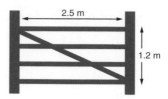

It is easy for Robert to cut the lengths of wood he needs for the horizontal bars, but he does not know how long the diagonal piece needs to be.

He could make a scale drawing and measure the length of the diagonal piece, but it would be much easier if there was a simple way to calculate the length. Luckily, there is!

 Measure the triangles below and find the areas of squares A, B and C in each diagram. What do you notice?

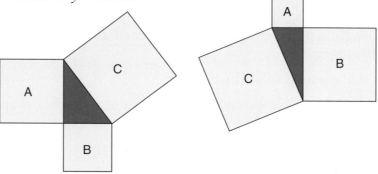

You should have found that the areas of the two smaller squares add up to the area of the largest square in each case.

This rule is called Pythagoras' rule (or theorem). It is true for all right-angled triangles. It is usually written like this:

$$a^2 + b^2 = c^2$$

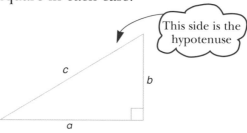

This side is the hypotenuse

The side labelled *c must* be the hypotenuse (the longest side, always the one opposite the right angle).

The diagonal bar on Robert's gate can be drawn as the hypotenuse of a right-angled triangle like this:

Pythagoras' rule is: $\quad a^2 + b^2 = c^2$

In this case: $\quad 2.5^2 + 1.2^2 = c^2$

$\qquad\quad\ 6.25 + 1.44 = c^2$

$\qquad\quad\ 7.69 = c^2$

$\qquad\quad\ c = 2.77$

'Undo' the square by finding the square root.

So the diagonal piece on Robert's gate needs to be 2.77 m long.

1 Use Pythagoras' rule to find the length of the hypotenuse in the triangles below.

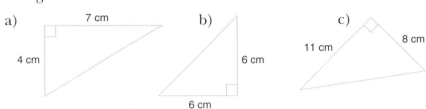

a) 7 cm, 4 cm

b) 6 cm, 6 cm

c) 11 cm, 8 cm

d) 9 cm, 10 cm

e) 6.6 cm, 4.8 cm

f) 8.3 cm, 3.9 cm

2 A field is 150 metres long and 120 metres wide. A footpath goes diagonally across the field. How long is the footpath?

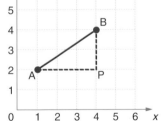

150 m

120 m

3 A ship sails 23 km due north and then 17 km due east. It then sails back to its starting point in a straight line. How far is the distance back to the starting point?

4 The diagram shows the two points A (1, 2) and B (4, 4).

a) What is the horizontal distance from A to the point P?

b) What is the vertical distance from B to the point P?

c) Use Pythagoras' rule to find the distance from A to B.

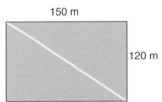

5 Use the same method as in question 4 to find the distances between each of the following pairs of points.

(You will find it helpful to draw diagrams showing the points.)

a) (3, 1) and (5, 6)   b) (4, 2) and (1, 5)

c) (−2, 4) and (3, 5)   d) (0, 3) and (−2, −1)

Finding one of the shorter sides

Terry is a window-cleaner. His ladder is 8 metres long.

For safety reasons he always places the foot of the ladder at least 1.5 metres from the wall. He wants to know how far up the wall he can make his ladder reach.

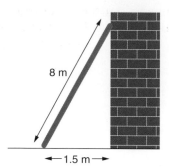

So far you have only been asked to find the length of the hypotenuse in a right-angled triangle. To solve Terry's problem, you need to be able to find one of the two shorter sides. You can use Pythagoras' rule to solve this kind of problem as well.

This is a simplified diagram of Terry's ladder.

y stands for the height up the wall that the ladder reaches.

Pythagoras' rule is
$$a^2 + b^2 = c^2$$

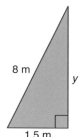

In this case
$$1.5^2 + y^2 = 8^2$$
$$2.25 + y^2 = 64$$

To find y^2, you need to subtract 2.25 from both sides of the equation.
$$y^2 = 61.75$$

Now you can find y by taking the square root of 61.75.
$$y = \sqrt{61.75} = 7.86$$

....

The ladder reaches 7.86 metres up the wall.

....

Remember!

   To find the hypotenuse, you have to **add**.

   To find one of the shorter sides, you have to **subtract**.

1 Find the lengths of the sides marked *x* in each of these triangles. In some of them you have to find the hypotenuse, in others you have to find one of the shorter sides.

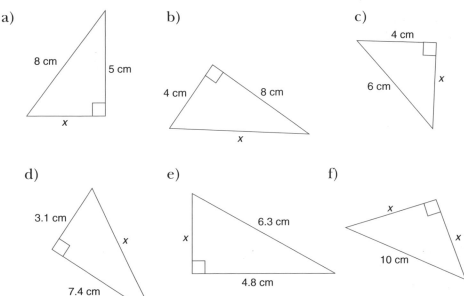

a) 8 cm, 5 cm, *x*

b) 4 cm, 8 cm, *x*

c) 4 cm, 6 cm, *x*

d) 3.1 cm, *x*, 7.4 cm

e) 6.3 cm, *x*, 4.8 cm

f) *x*, 10 cm, *x*

2 A ladder 6.2 metres long is to be placed so that it just reaches a window 5.7 metres from the ground. How far from the wall is the foot of the ladder?

3 The diagram shows an isosceles triangle split into two congruent right-angled triangles.

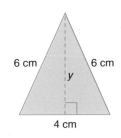

6 cm, *y*, 6 cm, 4 cm

a) Use Pythagoras' rule to find the height, *y*, of the triangle.

b) Find the area of the triangle.

4 The diagram shows a right-angled triangle ABC. The line BN has been drawn in, splitting the triangle into two smaller right-angled triangles ANB and CNB.

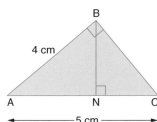

B, 4 cm, A, N, C, 5 cm

a) Work out the length of the side BC.

b) Using AB as the base of the triangle, work out the area of the triangle.

c) Using AC as the base of the triangle, use your answer to b) to work out the length of BN.

d) Work out the lengths of AN and CN.

Finishing off

Now that you have finished this chapter you should be able to

★ find the number of sides of a polygon if you know the interior angle

★ find out whether a shape tessellates

★ use the fact that the angle in a semicircle is a right angle

★ use Pythagoras' rule to find the hypotenuse of a right-angled triangle

★ use Pythagoras' rule to find one of the shorter sides of a right-angled triangle.

Use the questions in the next exercise to check that you understand everything.

Mixed exercise

1 Work out the number of sides of a regular polygon with interior angle

a) 140°   b) 60°   c) 156°

2 Which of the polygons in question 1 tessellate?

Explain how you worked it out in each case.

3 Work out each of the angles marked with letters in these diagrams.
Explain how you worked out each angle.

a)

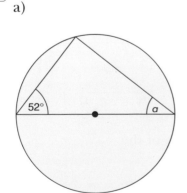

b)

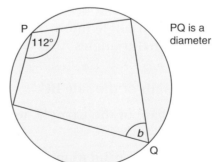

PQ is a diameter

4 Find the lengths of the sides marked with letters in these triangles.

a)

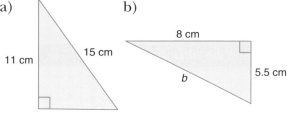

11 cm 15 cm *a*

b)

8 cm 5.5 cm *b*

c)

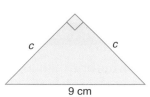

c *c* 9 cm

d)

8.9 cm 4.6 cm *d*

e)

e 7.7 cm 10.1 cm

f)

f 4.4 cm 3.2 cm

5 Find the distance between each pair of points.

a) (1, 4) and (4, 0)

b) (−2, 3) and (2, −1)

c) (−3, −4) and (−1, 1)

6 A ship leaves the port of Harwich (on the east coast) and sails 30 km. It is then 12 km north of Harwich.

How far east is it from Harwich?

Investigation

This triangle is a right-angled triangle.

$$3^2 + 4^2 = 9 + 16 = 25 = 5^2$$

The numbers 3, 4, 5 are called a **Pythagorean triple** because they obey Pythagoras' rule.

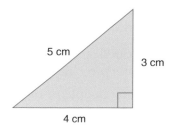

5 cm 3 cm 4 cm

Find as many different Pythagorean triples as you can.

(Don't count triples which are just a multiple of one you have already found, like 6, 8, 10 or 9, 12, 15, which are both multiples of 3, 4, 5.)

Four

Grouped data

Use the following questions to check that you still remember these topics.

Revision exercise

1 For each of these, say whether the data described are discrete or continuous.

a) The number of cars using a car park each day.

b) The weight of food waste from a school kitchen each day.

c) The number of patients admitted to a hospital each week.

d) The length of time that patients wait in an accident and emergency unit.

e) The annual rainfall in Luton.

2 A company is planning to sell red, green, blue and white T-shirts. The marketing manager asks Alison to do a survey to find out the popularity of the colours.

Alison conducts a survey of 270 people and produces this pie chart from her results.

a) How many people in the survey preferred blue?

b) How many preferred green?

c) Draw a bar chart and a pictogram to illustrate Alison's data.

d) Alison has to choose one of these displays for her report. Which would you choose?

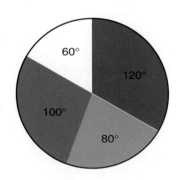

3 Carl is a keen dog-breeder. He wants to start to breed St Bernards. He visits Ruth, who is already an established breeder of St Bernards, to find out about it.

Carl has written down these questions to ask Ruth.

Ruth says, 'All the information you want is on there,' showing Carl this vertical line chart that she keeps on her wall.

a) How many litters have you reared?
b) How many pups have you reared?
c) What is the most usual number of pups in a litter?
d) How variable is the size of a litter?
e) What is the average number of pups per litter?

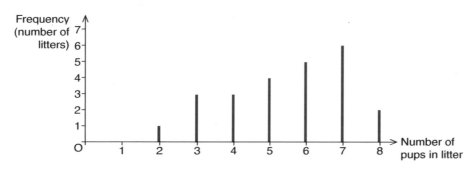

For each of Carl's questions, write down the mathematical name for the figure he is seeking, and use the graph to find its value.

4 Tim's youth club holds a ten-pin bowling evening. Tim organises the members into 6 teams of 6 players each, trying to mix experienced and inexperienced players. Half way through the match, the scores are as follows.

Team	A	B	C	D	E	F
Scores	12 37	21 15	47 66	9 45	51 19	56 67
	61 26	11 68	15 17	54 23	41 17	63 57
	49 10	21 42	14 33	25 27	65 29	30 21

a) Construct a tally chart with the individual scores in groups 0–9, 10–19, etc.

b) Draw up a frequency table for the grouped data.

c) What is the modal group?

d) James has scored 33 and says he is in the top half. Is he right?

e) What is the range of the individual scores?

f) Work out the total score for each team. Do you think Tim has made the teams reasonably evenly matched?

Grouping continuous data

Clare and Fulvio measure the height, h cm, of everyone in their drama group.

165.3	176.0	176.1	168.1	169.5
165.9	167.4	170.0	178.9	169.9
169.2	173.8	165.8	168.4	185.8

They want to display the data and Fulvio starts to draw a vertical line chart. He has not got very far when Clare stops him.

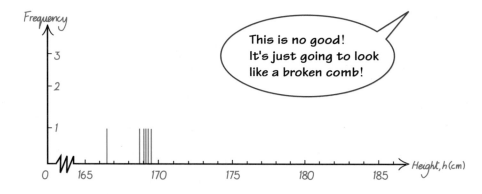

This is no good! It's just going to look like a broken comb!

 Do you agree with Clare's comment?

Clare draws up this grouped frequency table.

Height, h (cm)	$165 \leq h < 170$	$170 \leq h < 175$	$175 \leq h < 180$	$180 \leq h < 185$	$185 \leq h < 190$
Frequency (number of people)	9	2	3	0	1

Notice that Clare uses different symbols at each end of an interval.

$\leq$ means 'is less than or equal to', $<$ means 'is less than'.

Clare is the person with height 169.9 cm. Jem is 170.0 cm. Which groups are Clare and Jem in?

 Clare now draws a graph to illustrate the data. It is called a histogram.

Notice that

- there are no gaps between the bars

- the horizontal scale is continuous

- the vertical scale is described as 'frequency per 5 cm interval'. This means that bars of equal *area* represent equal frequencies.

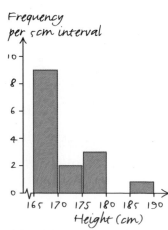

1 A company buys new cars for its fleet in batches of 12, and sells them after exactly one year. The mileage, *m*, on cars in one batch for sale are as follows.

23 147	18 219	46 351	33 337
16 517	23 474	25 012	29 830
29 216	9051	41 607	31 412

a) Make a grouped frequency table for these figures using intervals $0 \leq m < 10\,000$, $10\,000 \leq m < 20\,000$ and so on.

b) Draw a histogram to illustrate the data.

c) Two garages want to buy the cars. Here are the deals they offer.

Garage A

Mileage, *m*	Price (£)
$0 \leq m < 10\,000$	12 000
$10\,000 \leq m < 20\,000$	11 000
$20\,000 \leq m < 30\,000$	10 000
$30\,000 \leq m < 40\,000$	9 000
$40\,000 \leq m < 50\,000$	8 000

Garage B

Mileage, *m*	Price (£)
$0 \leq m < 20\,000$	13 000
$20\,000 \leq m < 40\,000$	10 000
$40\,000 \leq m < 60\,000$	7 000

Which garage should the company deal with if

(i) the deal is for all the cars?

(ii) the deal is for any number of cars?

State the total price in each case.

2 Car speedometers are being tested for accuracy at a road safety laboratory. In one 75 mph test, 30 speedometers are tested and their readings are as shown below.

71.8	73.6	72.8	74.7	73.7	74.8	74.1	75	74.3	75.2
73.8	72.1	76.7	73.9	74.8	73.2	76.8	76.2	74.7	74.4
72.3	76.9	72.9	75.4	74.9	77	74.1	75.1	74.2	77.2

a) Group these readings into classes 70 but less than 71 mph, 71 but less than 72 mph, etc. Think carefully about how you label these classes.

b) Draw a histogram to show these readings.

c) How many of the readings are in error by more than 4%?

Grouping rounded data

A bus company plans to start a new long distance service between two cities. They need to know how long the journey will take, so they do 15 trial runs. Each time the driver tells the company how long he took, to the nearest minute.

165	176	176	168	170
166	167	170	179	170
169	174	166	168	186

> 165 minutes 20 seconds is recorded as 165.
> 165 minutes 50 seconds is recorded as 166

Back in the office Tom has to display the data. He starts by making this grouped frequency table.

TIME (MINUTES)	165 – 169	170 – 174	175 – 179	180 – 184	185 – 180
FREQUENCY (NO. OF BUSES)	7	4	3	0	1

When Tom draws the histogram he marks the ends of the bars at $164\frac{1}{2}$, $169\frac{1}{2}$, $174\frac{1}{2}$ and so on. The diagram below shows why.

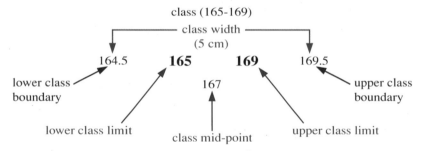

Here is Tom's histogram. He has also drawn in a frequency polygon in green, joining the mid-points of the tops of the bars.

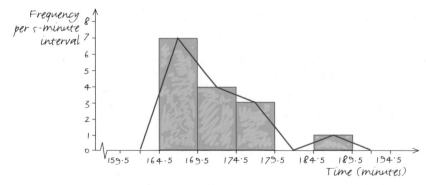

 Which display do you find more helpful, the histogram or the frequency polygon?

 The figures used in this example are the same as those on page 44, but rounded to the nearest whole number. Why are the histograms not the same?

1 The lengths (in minutes, to the nearest minute) of the phone calls made between Jill and Katharine are given in the table.

Time in minutes	1–5	6–10	11–15	16–20
Frequency	15	25	10	5

a) What are the boundary values for the class 6–10?

b) What is the mid-point of the class 6–10?

c) What is the longest possible time for a phone call in this table?

d) What is the shortest possible time for a phone call in this table?

e) Draw a histogram to show these data.

2 The weights (in grams, to the nearest gram) of the packs of information sent out one day by an investment adviser are given in the table.

Weight in grams	1–70	71–140	141–210	211–280
Frequency	350	420	560	79

a) What are the boundary values for the class 71–140?

b) What is the mid-point of the class 71–140?

c) What is the largest possible range for the data in this table?

d) Draw a histogram to show these data.

3 A group of 30 office workers went out for an office party. Their ages were as follows.

24	24	28	27	36	42	45	23	29	30
23	25	32	67	21	17	18	35	21	33
23	54	35	36	24	34	23	25	28	29

a) Construct a tally chart and frequency table for these data for the groups 16–20, 21–25, 26–30, 31–35, and so on.

b) Draw a histogram to show these data, taking care to label the ends of the intervals correctly.

c) The following Christmas the same people went out again. Describe how you could relabel your diagram.

4 On the opposite page, a frequency polygon has been added to the histogram of times.

a) Find the total area in the five rectangles of the histogram.

b) Find the area enclosed by the frequency polygon. What do you notice?

Mean, median and mode of grouped data

Debbie organises coach tours. She keeps a computer record of the age-group of each person booked on a particular tour. When she is ready to make the detailed arrangements for a tour she prints out a histogram like this one. She can then try to suit the activities and timings to their ages.

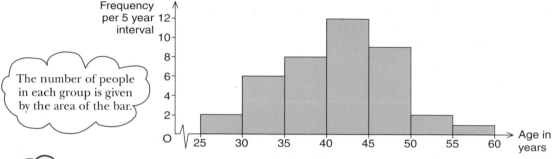

> The number of people in each group is given by the area of the bar.

How many people on this trip are aged 25–29?

What is the modal age group?

How can you estimate the mean age of the people booked on this tour?

It is impossible to work out the mean of grouped data accurately. You need the raw data. However, you can make an estimate like this.

Age	20–24	25–29	30–34	35–39	40–44	45–49	50–54	55–59	
Mid-point of age group	22	27	32	37	42	47	52	57	
Frequency (number of people)	0	2	6	8	12	9	2	1	Total 40
Mid-point × frequency	0	54	192	296	504	423	104	57	Total 1630

> This is the total number of people

> This is an estimate of the total age of this group - it assumes they are all 47

> This is an estimate of the total age of all the people

$$\text{Mean age of people} = \frac{\text{total age}}{\text{total number of people}}$$

$$\approx \frac{1630}{40}$$

$$\text{Mean age} \approx 40.75$$

Estimate the new mean when Frank Heys (aged 54) drops out of the tour.

1 Each passenger on a flight to Cairo is allowed one item of hand-luggage. The weights, to the nearest kilogram, of the hand-luggage items are given in the table.

Weight (kg)	1–5	6–10	11–15	16–20
Frequency (no. of items)	12	24	10	4

a) Which is the modal class?
b) What is the mid-point of the 6–10 kg class?
c) Estimate the total weight of hand-luggage on the plane.
d) Estimate the mean weight of the items.

2 Ben works for an estate agency which earns a percentage of the house price for each house it sells. He is working out the mean and mode of the house prices for the last year's sales, in order to prepare a cashflow forecast for the next year. He uses this table.

PRICE (£ THOUSANDS)	31-40	41-50	51-60	61-70	71-140
FREQUENCY (NO OF HOUSES)	35	42	56	7	3

a) Which is the modal class?
b) What is the mid-point of the class '71–140'?
c) Estimate the mean of these data.

3 In a recent cross-country skiing championship, the times for the first hundred competitors were recorded as follows.

Time (minutes)	80–84	85–89	90–94	95–99	100–104	105–109
Frequency (number of skiers)	8	27	33	20	8	4

a) Which is the modal class?
b) Estimate the mean time taken by these hundred skiers.

The fastest skier in this table was actually disqualified, so another skier whose time was 107 minutes entered the top hundred skiers.

c) Estimate the new mean time for the top hundred.
d) What is the new modal class for the top hundred?

Find the mean height of the people in your class or maths group.

Do it first using the individual heights, then from a grouped frequency table (if possible using a spreadsheet). Compare the answers you get by these two methods.

Quartiles

Neil is preparing a report on salary levels in his company. He draws up a cumulative frequency table and then plots the cumulative frequency curve.

SALARY, S (£ THOUSANDS)	$10 \leq S < 15$	$15 \leq S < 20$	$20 \leq S < 25$	$25 \leq S < 30$	$30 \leq S < 35$	$35 \leq S < 40$	$40 \leq S < 45$	$45 \leq S < 50$
FREQUENCY (NO. OF EMPLOYEES)	10	105	49	20	10	3	2	1
LESS THAN	15	20	25	30	35	40	45	50
CUMULATIVE FREQUENCY	10	115	164	184	194	197	199	200

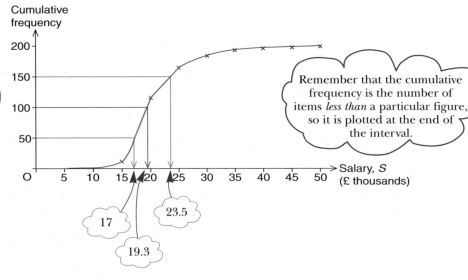

There are 200 employees in total, so the median is the 100th value, and the lower and upper quartiles are the 50th and 150th values.

Remember that the cumulative frequency is the number of items *less than* a particular figure, so it is plotted at the end of the interval.

17

19.3

23.5

The red line shows how Neil estimates the median salary. The green and blue lines show how he estimates the lower and upper quartile salaries.

What proportion of the employees earn less than £19 300?

What proportion earn less than £17 000?

What proportion earn between £17 000 and £23 500?

In a negotiation between the union and the management, the union representative quotes the modal salary range as £15 000 – £20 000.

The management representative estimates the mean salary from Neil's table as £20 925.

Explain how she reaches this estimate.

Why do you think the management representative prefers to use this figure?

How can you estimate the salary range from Neil's table?

1 The table shows the number of days that a factory's employees have been absent due to sickness.

Number of days lost per year		Frequency
At least	**Less than**	**(number of employees)**
0	5	34
5	10	56
10	15	38
15	20	15
20	25	10
25	30	4
30	35	2
35	40	1

a) Represent the data on a cumulative frequency diagram.
b) Use your graph to estimate the median and the inter-quartile range.
c) Estimate the number of employees who missed fewer than 12 days.
d) Estimate the number of employees who missed more than 23 days.

2 The table shows the number of children still swimming after different numbers of lengths in a sponsored swim. Fifty children started.

Number of completed lengths	2	4	6	8	10	12	14
Number of children still swimming	50	44	34	16	8	3	0
Number stopping	0	6					

a) Copy and complete the table so that it shows how many children stopped at each stage as well as how many carried on.

b) Draw a graph of the number of children still swimming after each number of lengths. This is a reversed cumulative frequency curve – it shows how many children have swum *more than* (not less than) a certain distance.

c) On the same axes, draw a graph of the number of children stopping. What shape is this?

d) The graph in part c) is a mirror image of the graph in part b). What is the line of symmetry?

Draw a cumulative frequency curve of the heights of your class.
Find the median and the inter-quartile range. Put this chart on the wall next to the histogram.

Making comparisons

Many professional basketball players are very tall. Imran collects these data on the heights of 120 basketballers and 120 footballers (all to the nearest whole inch).

Height (inches)	70	71	72	73	74	75	76	77	78	79	80	81
Footballers	0	12	24	31	34	12	4	2	1	0	0	0
Basketballers	0	0	0	0	4	10	25	37	25	12	7	0

He draws these two frequency polygons showing the players' heights.

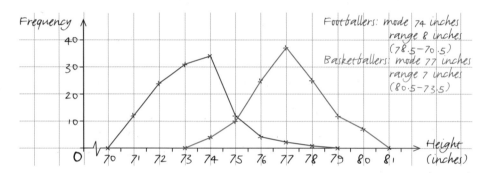

 What does this graph tell you?

Imran decides to plot cumulative frequency curves for the same data.

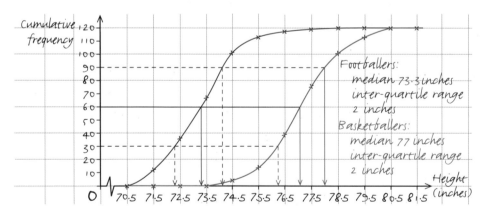

 What does this graph tell you that the other one does not?

Which graph do you find more helpful for comparing the heights of footballers and basketball players?

1 Emma has done a survey of the number of items in people's shopping baskets at the checkouts of two different shops. Here are her results.

Number of items	1-5	6-10	11-15	16-20	21-25	26-30	31-35
Frequency: shop A	24	49	13	8	4	2	0
Frequency: shop B	5	8	15	33	29	10	0

a) Which is the modal group for each shop?

b) On the same set of axes, draw the frequency polygon for each shop.

c) Compare the frequency polygons. What do they tell you about the two shops?

d) Suggest what type of shop each might be.

2 This table shows the results of a survey that was done to check the phasing of the traffic lights at the site of some major roadworks. The time spent waiting by 200 cars travelling in each direction was recorded one morning.

Delay, t (minutes)	$0 \leq t < 2$	$2 \leq t < 4$	$4 \leq t < 6$	$6 \leq t < 8$	$8 \leq t < 10$	$10 \leq t < 12$	$12 \leq t < 14$	$14 \leq t < 16$
North-bound	50	80	60	10	0	0	0	0
South-bound	10	25	35	55	45	20	10	0

a) On the same set of axes, draw a cumulative frequency curve for the delay times in each direction.

b) Estimate the median and the inter-quartile range for each direction.

c) Do you think the traffic lights are sensibly phased?

d) Might the survey have produced different results at a different time of the day?

Rewrite the height data you collected on page 49 in separate frequency tables for boys and girls. (Ideally you need the same number of boys and girls.) Use frequency polygons and cumulative frequency curves to compare the heights of the boys and the girls.

Finishing off

The questions in the next exercise check that you understand everything covered in this chapter as well as some extra topics from Intermediate Book 1.

Mixed exercise

1 The following information on the birth weight of 200 babies born at Avonford General Infirmary was collected as part of a national survey of birth weights.

Weight in kg	1.5–1.9	2.0–2.4	2.5–2.9	3.0–3.4	3.5–3.9	4.0–4.4	4.5–4.9	5.0–5.4
Frequency (no. of babies)	8	18	40	52	38	22	16	6

a) Draw a histogram to display these data.
b) Estimate the mean birth weight of the babies.
c) State the modal class for these data.
d) Draw a cumulative frequency curve for the birth weights, and use it to estimate the median and the inter-quartile range.
e) The mean weight for babies born in the UK as a whole is 3.25 kg, and the lower and upper quartiles are 2.9 kg and 3.6 kg. How do these Avonford babies compare with the national figures?

2 A manufacturer of children's clothes is changing its sizing policy to be according to height rather than age. Size 1 is to be for children 100 – 108 cm tall, size 2 is to be for children 108 – 116 cm tall, and so on.

The company conducts a survey of the heights of 100 girls and 100 boys to find out the proportion of children of each size. Here are the results for girls between 5 and 10 years of age.

Height (cm)	$100 \leq h < 108$	$108 \leq h < 116$	$116 \leq h < 124$	$124 \leq h < 132$	$132 \leq h < 140$
Frequency (no. of girls)	12	18	30	25	15

a) Draw a histogram to display the data.
b) Of which size should the company make most girls' clothes?
c) A production run of 5000 garments is planned. How many should be of each size?

3 Overtime is expensive. Sam is the manager of a production line, and he is wondering whether it would be cheaper to employ extra workers instead of paying for so much overtime by existing staff. He makes this table to show the overtime hours worked by his staff in one week.

Hours overtime	$0 \leqslant h < 4$	$4 \leqslant h < 8$	$8 \leqslant h < 12$	$12 \leqslant h < 16$	$16 \leqslant h < 20$	$20 \leqslant h < 24$
Frequency	12	22	9	1	1	5

a) Estimate the mean number of hours of overtime per worker.

b) Draw a cumulative frequency curve, and use it to estimate the median number of hours of overtime worked.

c) Why are the estimated mean and median different?

d) The working week at Sam's company is 35 hours. Each worker on the production line is paid £6 per hour during normal hours and £9 per hour for overtime. Do you think, from these figures, that Sam would be better off employing more workers?

4 In a recent canoe slalom the times of the first 100 competitors were recorded.

John is training to enter next year's event, and his coach is analysing the competition.

He makes this table of the number of seconds by which the competitors' times exceeded 2 minutes.

a) Construct a cumulative frequency diagram.

b) Estimate the median time.

c) Estimate the inter-quartile range.

d) John's practice time is 2 minutes, 12 seconds. What position can he expect in the competition?

Time	Number of competitors
0–4	8
5–9	27
10–14	33
15–19	20
20–24	8
25–29	4

5 Louise takes size 7 shoes, but her mother only takes size 4. Louise decides to do a quick survey of the size of her friends' feet and their mothers' feet, to see if the mothers' feet are generally smaller. Here are her data.

Name	Louise	Rachel	Kim	Jamila	Jess	Fiona	Anna	Tessa
Nearest whole shoe size	7	5	6	4	5	8	5	6
Mother's nearest whole shoe size	4	4	6	3	5	4	6	5

a) Make frequency tables for the daughters' and the mothers' shoe sizes, then draw two frequency polygons on the same set of axes.

b) Draw a scatter diagram of mother's shoe size against daughter's shoe size.

c) What do your graphs tell you?

6 Sara is a quality control officer. She is testing the lifetime of torch batteries by switching on 100 new torches and recording, for each torch, the time it takes for the battery to run down.

She produces this table of results.

Time (hours) before battery runs down	50	100	150	200	250
Cumulative frequency	10	35	68	85	100

a) Draw a cumulative frequency diagram for Sara's data.

b) Estimate the median and the inter-quartile range.

c) Estimate the number of torch batteries which exceeded the guaranteed lifetime of 130 hours.

d) The company wants to advertise a battery lifetime that 95% of batteries will reach. What lifetime should they quote?

7 Which of these descriptions fits the mode, which fits the median and which fits the mean?

It takes account of all the data items. Sometimes it comes out at an impossible value, like 2.4 children.

It's the value that occurs most often in the data. It has the highest column on a bar chart. Its value isn't affected by extreme values.

It's the middle value when the data are put in order. Its value isn't affected by extreme data values. You can estimate it from a cumulative frequency curve.

8 A company uses two types of car in its fleet (A and B). The fleet manager keeps these records of the distances travelled and the running costs for 20 of the cars.

Type A

Distance (thousands of miles)	5	5.6	6.9	7.7	9	9.9	9.9	11.1	11.8	13.1
Costs (hundreds of pounds)	6.3	7.7	8.5	9.8	9	10.1	11.5	11	12.7	13.4

Type B

Distance (thousands of miles)	4.5	5.6	6.3	7	8.2	9.4	11.1	12.1	12.5	13.3
Costs (hundreds of pounds)	7.9	8.6	8.9	9.3	9.8	10.2	10.6	11.3	11.1	12.3

a) For each type of car calculate the mean distance and the mean cost.

b) Plot these figures on a scatter diagram using one colour for Type A and a different colour for Type B.

c) This year the company expects to expand and distances will be 50% higher. From the graph, do you think the company should buy new cars of Type A or Type B?

9 Here are the times (to the nearest second) for a 100 m freestyle race and a 100 m sprint for fitness enthusiasts.

Name	Ann	Bob	Cal	Dave	Erin	Fiona	Geoff	Sunil	Helen	Tess
100 m freestyle	90	65	70	88	80	74	80	75	70	72
100 m sprint	13	11	12	13	13	11	15	14	11	13

a) Show these data in a scatter diagram.

b) Work out the mean sprint time and the mean freestyle time. Plot a point to show these mean times (use a different colour).

c) Draw a line of best fit of the points, going through your mean point.

d) What conclusions can you draw?

Five

Simultaneous equations

Using simultaneous equations

Lisa and George enter a fishing contest.

Their catches are recorded as shown.

The roach are all of a similar size – they are from the same shoal. The same is true of the perch.

After the contest the fish are put back and they swim away.

Later on, Lisa and George try to work out from their results the weights of a typical roach and perch.

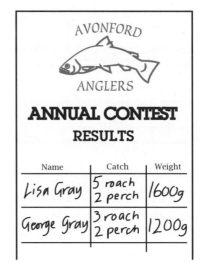

AVONFORD
ANGLERS

ANNUAL CONTEST
RESULTS

Name	Catch	Weight
Lisa Gray	5 roach 2 perch	1600g
George Gray	3 roach 2 perch	1200g

How can they work this out?

Puzzle it out, then discuss how you did it.

One approach is to write and solve a pair of **simultaneous equations**, as shown below.

Using r and p for the weights of a typical roach and perch, you can write

For Lisa's catch	$5r + 2p = 1600$	①
For George's catch	$3r + 2p = 1200$	②
Subtract ② from ①	$2r = 400$	
Divide by 2	$r = 200$	
Substitute $r = 200$ in ①	$5 \times 200 + 2p = 1600$	
	$1000 + 2p = 1600$	
Subtract 1000	$2p = 600$	
Divide by 2	$p = 300$	

① and ② are the simultaneous equations

Subtracting has got rid of the term in p. You now have an equation just in r, which you can solve

Once you have found r, you can find p by substitution

Check: substitute for r and p in the left-hand side of ②:

$3 \times 200 + 2 \times 300 = 1200$ ✓

The solution is $r = 200$, $p = 300$: a roach weighs about 200 g and a perch about 300 g.

Why is equation ② used for the check, rather than equation ①?

1 Write down this pair of equations. $2x + y = 15$ ①

$x + y = 8$ ②

Follow these steps to solve them.

a) Subtract ② from ① and so find x.

b) Substitute your answer for x in ① to find y.

c) Check that your answers fit equation ②.

2 Solve these pairs of simultaneous equations. (In some of them it is easier to subtract the first equation from the second.)

a) $2x + y = 17$
$x + y = 13$

b) $2x + y = 21$
$x + y = 11$

c) $x + y = 5$
$3x + y = 17$

d) $x + 4y = 10$
$2x + 4y = 12$

e) $2x + 3y = 19$
$x + 3y = 14$

f) $3x + 5y = 23$
$x + 5y = 11$

g) $5p + 7q = 40$
$2p + 7q = 37$

h) $6a + 5b = 1600$
$11a + 5b = 2100$

i) $4c + 19d = 49$
$11c + 19d = 35$

3 Solve the following equations. (Remember when you subtract something from itself the answer is always zero. For example, $-y - (-y) = 0$.)

a) $5x - y = 32$
$x - y = 4$

b) $4x - 3y = 11$
$2x - 3y = 5$

c) $7x - 2y = 41$
$3x - 2y = 5$

d) $3x - y = 3$
$x - y = 1$

e) $3x - 4y = 10$
$5x - 4y = 14$

f) $2x - 2y = 9$
$4x - 2y = 19$

4 Ella sends Sally out to buy 5 packs of white paper and 2 packs of blue paper. The bill comes to £15. The next day Ella sends Sally for 7 packs of white and 2 packs of blue. This time the bill is £19.

What is the price of each type of paper?

5 Use the information below to form two equations.
Solve them to find the cost of 1 orange and the cost of 1 apple.

£1·30

£1·50

More simultaneous equations

Look at this pair of equations.

$$7p + 3q = 76 \quad ①$$
$$p - 3q = 4 \quad ②$$

 What happens when you subtract ② from ①?

In this case, subtracting one equation from the other does not **eliminate** q. Instead you have to add the equations.

$$7p + 3q = 76 \quad ①$$
$$p - 3q = 4 \quad ②$$

Add $\qquad\qquad 8p \quad\quad = 80$ ← *q is now eliminated*

Divide by 8 $\qquad\qquad p = 10$

Substitute for p in ① $\quad 70 + 3q = 76$

Subtract 70 $\qquad\qquad 3q = 6$

Divide by 3 $\qquad\qquad q = 2$

The solution is $p = 10$, $q = 2$.

 Check that this solution fits equation ②.

In many cases, neither adding nor subtracting the equations eliminates an unknown.

For example, look at these.

$$5a + 6b = 124 \quad ①$$
$$7a + 2b = 148 \quad ②$$

 Try adding and subtracting to eliminate an unknown.

In this case, you need to spot that multiplying ② by 3 gives you $6b$ in two equations.

② × 3 $\qquad\qquad 21a + 6b = 444 \quad ③$ ← *Remember to multiply both sides by 3*

Subtract ① from ③ $\qquad \dfrac{5a + 6b = 124}{16a \qquad\;\; = 320}$

Divide by 16 $\qquad\qquad a \qquad\quad = 20$

Although this equation is labelled ③ actually it is just equation ② written in a different way

 Use this value of a to find b. Check your solution.

Why is it better to subtract ① from ③ rather than the other way round?

Describe how you would solve

$$2x + y = 17$$
$$3x - 2y = 8$$

1 Solve these equations.

a) $8x + 3y = 86$
$4x - 3y = 34$

b) $x + y = 21$
$2x - y = 33$

c) $5x + 4y = 60$
$8x - 4y = 44$

d) $14y - 3x = 43$
$2y + 3x = 37$

e) $9a - 5b = 68$
$2a + 5b = 9$

f) $3p + 7q = 45$
$3p - 7q = 24$

2 Write down these equations.

$$3x + 4y = 22 \quad ①$$
$$5x - y \ = 52 \quad ②$$

a) Multiply ② by 4. Call the 'new' equation ③.

b) Add ③ to ①.

c) Find x and substitute in ① to find y.

d) Check your solution in ②.

3 Solve these equations. Don't forget you can use your calculator to help with the arithmetic.

a) $2x + 3y = 73$
$11x - y = 209$

b) $6x + 5y = 8$
$4x + y = 3$

c) $3x - 2y = 20$
$8x - y = 75$

d) $2x + y = 12$
$5x - 4y = 17$

e) $2x - 3y = 7$
$4x - 7y = 13$

f) $2x + 3y = 15$
$4x + 7y = 34$

g) $5x + 2y = 47$
$7x - 8y = 28$

h) $6x - 5y = 50$
$x + 7y = 24$

i) $11x - 4y = 498$
$18x - 12y = 744$

4 Melissa is buying doughnuts for her family. Most of her family prefer jam ones. She has worked out these possible combinations.

9 jam + 1 ring ⟶ £1·74
7 jam + 4 ring ⟶ £1·74

Work out the price of each type of doughnut.

How many jam doughnuts could she buy for £2?

5 Carl and his father share the same birthday. Carl's father was 32 when Carl was born.

Today when Carl adds his father's age to his own age the answer is 100 exactly.

How old is Carl and how old is his father?

Multiplying both equations

 How would you solve this pair of simultaneous equations?

$3x + 5y = 19$ ①

$7x - 4y = 60$ ②

This is how Karen solves them.

$$① \times 7 \quad 21x + 35y = 133$$
$$② \times 3 \quad 21x - 12y = 180$$
$$\text{Subtract} \qquad\qquad 47y = -47$$
$$\text{Divide by 47} \qquad\quad y = -1$$

> Remember that
> $35y - (-12y) = 35y + 12y$

$$\text{Substitute in} ① \quad 3x + 5 \times (-1) = 19$$
$$3x - 5 \qquad = 19$$
$$3x \qquad\quad = 24$$
$$\text{Add 5}$$
$$\text{Divide by 3} \qquad x \qquad\quad = 8$$

$$\text{Check in} ②$$
$$7x - 4y = 7 \times 8 - 4 \times (-1)$$
$$= 56 + 4$$
$$= 60 \quad ✓$$

and so $\underline{x = 8, \ y = -1}$

This is how Saleen solves them.

$$① \times 4: \quad 12x + 20y = 76$$
$$② \times 5: \quad 35x - 20y = 300$$
$$\text{Add}: \qquad\quad 47x \qquad = 376 \qquad \text{so } \underline{x = 8}$$

$$\text{Substitute into} ①: \quad 24 + 5y = 19$$
$$5y = -5$$
$$\text{so } \underline{y = -1}$$

 Do you think one method is easier than the other?

Can you find a method for which you only have to multiply one of the equations?

 Instead of subtracting, some people find it easier to change all the signs in the bottom equation. Then they can add it to the top one.

Why does this work?

> If subtracting's bad
> Change the sign
> On the bottom line
> Then add!

1 Write down this pair of equations.

$$3x + 5y = 290 \quad ①$$
$$5x - 2y = 70 \quad ②$$

Follow these steps to solve them.

a) Multiply equation ① by 2.

b) Multiply equation ② by 5.

c) Add your two new equations.

d) Find x and y and check your answers.

2 Solve each pair of equations.

a) $2x + 3y = 24$
   $3x - 2y = 23$

b) $3x + 5y = 24$
   $5x + 4y = 40$

c) $3x - 2y = 26$
   $4x - 5y = 30$

d) $7x - 6y = 41$
   $2x + 5y = 5$

e) $2x + 7y = 35$
   $5x + 3y = 15$

f) $10x - 4y = 1$
   $16x - 3y = 5$

g) $6x - 5y = 19$
   $9x - 2y = 67$

h) $4x + 11y = 260$
   $15x + 2y = 190$

3 Bavinder makes desserts to sell in the family shop. She makes them in big trays and cuts them into portions. A tray of barfi sells for a total of £18 and a tray of halwa sells for £21.

The barfi takes about 45 minutes per tray to prepare and cook, and the halwa takes about 25 minutes per tray.

One morning Bavinder cooks for 5 hours. All her desserts are sold, and the takings from them are £153.

How many trays of barfi and how many trays of halwa did Bavinder make?

4 David and Sian work part-time at Pizza Palace. After 11 p.m. they are paid at a higher rate.

Last week David was paid £149 for 34 hours' work at basic rate and 5 hours at the higher rate.

Sian was paid £229 for 50 hours at the basic rate and 9 hours at the higher rate.

What is the basic hourly rate and the rate after 11 p.m.?

5 Jess is a florist. She is preparing the flowers for a wedding.

For the bride's bouquet Jess uses 10 roses and 6 carnations. For each bridesmaid's posy she uses 4 roses and 5 carnations.

The flowers cost her £12 for the bouquet and £6.10 for each posy.

What is the cost per bloom of roses and of carnations?

Other methods of solution

Using graphs

Each Saturday Rob and Ed go to the cinema with friends. Some of them are under 15 and so they get cheaper tickets. Last week only one friend went with them. This equation shows how the group was made up, and the total cost.

$$2x + y = 10 \quad ①$$

What was the total cost? What do x and y represent?

Write down some possible values of x and y.

The equation for the previous week, when there were more people is

$$4x + 3y = 24 \quad ②$$

The graph of each of these equations is a straight line. You can see that the lines cross at the point $(3, 4)$.

At this point the x and y values satisfy both equations, so the solution to the problem is $x = 3, y = 4$.

In other words the cost of tickets is £3 for the under-15s and £4 for the others.

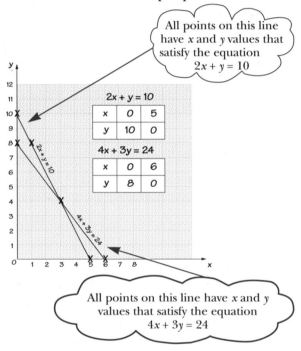

All points on this line have x and y values that satisfy the equation $2x + y = 10$

2x + y = 10		
x	0	5
y	10	0

4x + 3y = 24		
x	0	6
y	8	0

All points on this line have x and y values that satisfy the equation $4x + 3y = 24$

Check that you get the same answer using algebra.

Which method do you find easier?

Using substitution

Another way to solve simultaneous equations is by substitution, as shown below.

$$y = 2x \quad ①$$
$$4x + 3y = 35 \quad ②$$

Substitute for y in ②	$4x + 3 \times 2x = 35$
(Tidy up)	$10x = 35$
Divide by 10	$x = 3.5$
Substitute for x in ①	$y = 7$

Substitution is a good method when at least one of the equations is in the form $y = mx + c$

The solution is $x = 3.5, y = 7$.

Which method would you use for the equations $x = 3y + 7$ and $2x - y = 24$?

64

1 Solve each of these pairs of equations using a graph.

For a) to c) draw your x and y axes from 0 to 10.

a) $x + 2y = 16$
    $2x + y = 14$

b) $x + y = 16$
    $5x + 3y = 60$

c) $3x + 4y = 24$
    $x + y = 7$

For d) to f) draw your x axis from 0 to 10 and your y axis from -10 to $+10$.

d) $x + y = 6$
    $2x - y = 9$

e) $5x + y = 25$
    $x - 2y = 16$

f) $x + 3y = 7$
    $4x - y = 2$

2 a) Mike collects x 200 g jars and y 400 g jars to qualify for a free mug.

Write down an equation connecting x and y.

Draw a graph of this equation using axes for x from 0 to 12, and y from 0 to 10.

b) Mike has bought 8 jars of coffee altogether.

Write down a second equation connecting x and y.

Draw the graph of this equation on the same axes.

c) Use your graphs to find how many jars of each size Mike has bought.

COLLECT
12 VOUCHERS
and get this mug
FREE !

Aroma

Each 200g jar of
Aroma coffee carries
1 VOUCHER
Each 400g jar of
Aroma coffee carries
2 VOUCHERS

3 Caroline wants to buy 80 Christmas cards this year. She can do this by buying 8 packets and 2 boxes or 4 packets and 3 boxes.

Write down two equations to show this information.

Solve them by a graphical method to find how many cards are in each packet and each box.

4 Solve each of these pairs of equations by substitution.

a) $y = 2x + 1$
    $5x - 2y = 33$

b) $3x + 2y = 16$
    $y = 4x - 3$

c) $y = x - 2$
    $y = 8 - 3x$

d) $2y + 3x = 7$
    $y = 4 - x$

e) $y = 2x - 3$
    $x - y = 2$

f) $y = 7 - x$
    $2x + 3y = 15$

Investigation

What happens when you try to solve the following pairs of equations by an algebraic method?

a) $4x - 2y = 6$
    $10x - 5y = 15$

b) $3x + y = 6$
    $3x + y = 12$

Draws graphs for each pair of lines and use them to help you to explain your results.

Finishing off

Now that you have finished this chapter you should be able to

★ solve simultaneous equations using algebra

★ solve simultaneous equations using graphs.

Use the following questions to check that you understand everything.

Mixed exercise

1 Solve these equations. In some cases you can add or subtract the equations straight away, but in others you need to multiply first. (Remember that you need to find both unknowns.)

a) $x + y = 13$
$x - y = 3$

b) $x + 5y = 3$
$x - 4y = 12$

c) $7p + 4q = 19$
$2p + q = 5$

d) $5a - 2b = 7$
$8a - 4b = 10$

e) $4x - y = 300$
$3x - 2y = 0$

f) $2x + 3y = 16$
$3x - 2y = 11$

g) $3s + 2t = 26$
$2s - 3t = 26$

h) $2c + 7d = 19$
$5c - 2d = 28$

i) $2x + 11y = 52$
$4x - 11y = 5$

j) $3x + 20y = 25$
$4x + 10y = 25$

k) $4x - 3y = 50$
$5x - 2y = 80$

l) $2x + 5y = 72$
$11x - 2y = 101$

m) $2x - 3y = 34$
$11x - y = 1$

n) $5x + 7y = 6$
$7x - 3y = 2$

o) $9x + 10y = 57$
$3x + 2y = 15$

p) $4x - y = 36$
$8x + 2y = 88$

q) $3x + 5y = 22$
$2x + 3y = 14$

r) $x + y = 1$
$9x + 10y = 11$

s) $22x + 3y = 116$
$2x - 5y = 0$

t) $3x - 8y = -21$
$7x - 5y = -8$

u) $7p + 2q = 8$
$2p - 3q = 13$

2 Mike and Julia have been saving for a while. If they put their savings together they have a total of £1300. Mike has saved £200 more than Julia.

Write down two simultaneous equations to express this information, and solve them to find out how much each has saved.

3 Miranda asks Rupal to record her two favourite soap operas while she is away on holiday.

Rupal works out that, using all 480 minutes on the tape, she can record 10 episodes of *Northerners* and 9 of *The Village*, or 8 episodes of *Northerners* and 12 of *The Village*.

How long are the episodes of each soap?

Would it be possible to record an equal number of episodes of each soap, and to use up all the tape?

4 The sum of two numbers is 21 and their difference is 5.

Write down two equations to represent this information, and solve them to find the two numbers.

(The sum of x and y is $x + y$ and their difference is $x - y$.)

5 The Scotts and the Masons buy tickets for a pantomime.

The Scotts buy tickets for 2 adults and 3 children at a cost of £36.

The Masons buy tickets for 4 adults and 2 children at a cost of £48.

a) Work out the cost of an adult's ticket and a child's ticket.

It turns out that 2 of the adults in the Mason party (the grandparents) are entitled to the cheaper tickets because they are over 60.

b) How much refund should the Masons receive?

6 A company makes two types of medical instrument.

Instrument A takes 4 machine-hours and 7 operator-hours to make.

Instrument B takes 9 machine-hours and 8 operator-hours.

Find how many of each type of instrument the company makes in a week when it devotes 550 machine-hours and 730 operator-hours to making them.

7 Solve these pairs of equations using graphs.

a) $x + y = 18$
$4x + 3y = 60$

b) $2x + 5y = 40$
$2x - y = 16$

c) $x - y = 4$
$6x + 7y = 63$

8 Solve each of these pairs of equations by substitution.

a) $y = 3x + 2$
$3x + 2y = 13$

b) $y = 5x + 1$
$y = 7x - 2$

c) $2x - 3y = 9$
$y = 2x - 3$

Six

Trigonometry

Before you start this chapter you should

- ★ understand what similar shapes are

- ★ know that angles round a point add up to 360° and that angles on a straight line add up to 180°

- ★ know that the angle sum of a triangle is 180°

- ★ understand and be able to use bearings.

Introduction to trigonometry

Trigonometry is the study of triangles. In this chapter you will learn how to calculate sides and angles in right-angled triangles.

You need a scientific calculator for this chapter.

Triangles A, B and C are all right-angled triangles, and they all have an angle of 30°. This means that they are all enlargements of each other, with different scale factors. They are **similar** triangles.

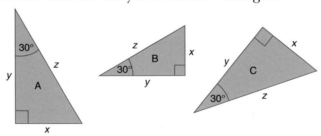

- ● The sides marked *z* in the diagram are all opposite to the right-angle. They are the longest sides of each triangle. These sides are called the **hypotenuse**.

- ● The sides marked *x* in the diagram are all **opposite** to the angle of 30°.

- ● The sides marked *y* in the diagram are all **adjacent** to (next to) the angle of 30°.

For any right-angled triangle with one angle marked, you can label the sides hypotenuse, opposite and adjacent.
(Some people use the abbreviations **hyp**, **opp** and **adj**.)

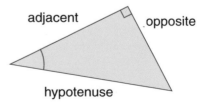

Exercise

1 Copy each of the triangles below and label the hypotenuse, opposite and adjacent sides.

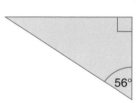

2 Triangles P, Q and R are similar triangles.

They all have an angle of 40°.

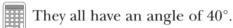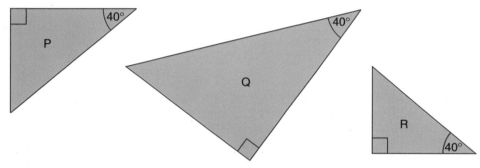

a) Measure the hypotenuse, opposite and adjacent sides of each triangle.

b) Work out the ratio $\dfrac{\text{opposite}}{\text{adjacent}}$ for each triangle.

c) Work out the ratio $\dfrac{\text{opposite}}{\text{hypotenuse}}$ for each triangle.

d) Work out the ratio $\dfrac{\text{adjacent}}{\text{hypotenuse}}$ for each triangle.

e) What do you notice?

3 Repeat question 2 for triangles X, Y and Z.

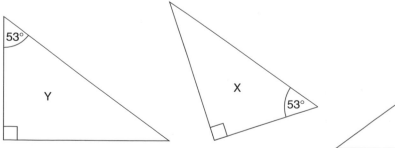

Using tangent (tan)

In the last exercise, you found out that in each of triangles P, Q and R, the ratio $\frac{\text{opposite}}{\text{adjacent}} = 0.84$ (2 d.p.).

This is true for all right-angled triangles with an angle of 40°.

In a similar way, in triangles X, Y, Z and all right-angled triangles with an angle of 53°, the ratio $\frac{\text{opposite}}{\text{adjacent}} = 1.33$ (2 d.p.).

For all right-angled triangles with a particular angle, the ratio $\frac{\text{opposite}}{\text{adjacent}}$ is a fixed number. This number is called the **tangent** (or **tan**) of that angle.

> tan 40° = 0.84
>
> tan 53° = 1.33

You can find the tan of an angle using a scientific calculator. First, make sure that your calculator is in Degree (Deg) mode. Now check that you know how to use the (tan) button. For some calculators you must enter the angle and then press the (tan) button. For others you must press (tan) first and then the angle, followed by ENTER or EXE.

Use your calculator to work out tan 40° *and* tan 53°. *Check that you get the answers shown above (although your calculator will give more decimal places).*

Try to find tan 90° *on your calculator. Why doesn't it work?*

Finding the opposite side using tan

The example below shows how you can use tan to find the length of *x*.

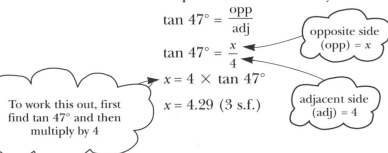

$$\tan 47° = \frac{\text{opp}}{\text{adj}}$$

$$\tan 47° = \frac{x}{4}$$

opposite side (opp) = x

$$x = 4 \times \tan 47°$$

$$x = 4.29 \text{ (3 s.f.)}$$

adjacent side (adj) = 4

To work this out, first find tan 47° and then multiply by 4

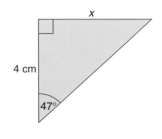

Did you get the same answer on your calculator? (You should have!)

1 Use a calculator to find these tangents. Give your answers to 3 decimal places.

   a) tan 25°   b) tan 73°   c) tan 45°

   d) tan 37°   e) tan 51°   f) tan 82°

2 Find the side marked *x* in each of the triangles below.

a)

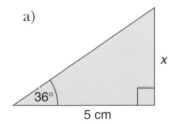

b)

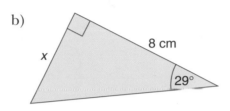

c)

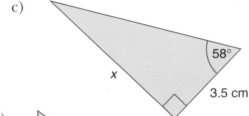

d)

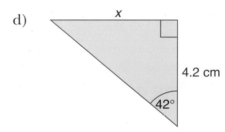

e)

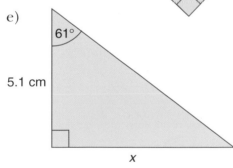

f)

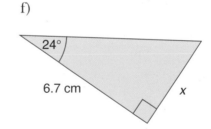

3 Jenna stands 50 m from the foot of a tall tree. She measures the angle between the ground and a line in the direction of the top of the tree (this is called the **angle of elevation**). She finds that the angle of elevation is 34°. How high is the tree?

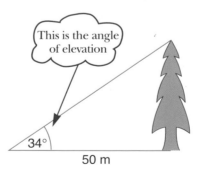

This is the angle of elevation

Measure the angle of elevation of a tall tree or building, and use it to work out its height.

Finding the adjacent side using tan

In the last exercise, all the lengths that you had to work out were opposite sides.

You can use tan to work out an adjacent side, as well.

Example

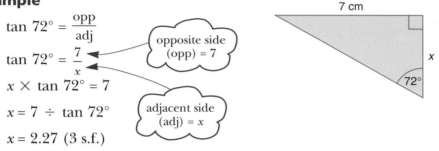

$$\tan 72° = \frac{opp}{adj}$$

$$\tan 72° = \frac{7}{x}$$

opposite side (opp) = 7

$$x \times \tan 72° = 7$$

$$x = 7 \div \tan 72°$$

adjacent side (adj) = x

$$x = 2.27 \ (3 \ \text{s.f.})$$

The adjacent side is 2.27 cm.

 Check that you get the same answer on your calculator.

Finding an angle using tan

You can also use tan to find the angle in a right-angled triangle if you know the opposite and adjacent sides. The example below shows how.

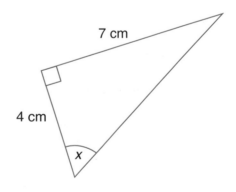

$$\tan x = \frac{opp}{adj}$$

$$\tan x = \frac{7}{4} = 1.75$$

You now need to find out what angle has a tan of 1.75. To do this you need to 'undo' tan. You can do this using a scientific calculator. The key you need may be labelled (tan⁻¹) or (arctan) or you may need to press (INV) followed by (tan). You may have to press the key before or after entering 1.75.

 Use your calculator to work out what angle has a tan of 1.75.

You should get the answer 60.3 (correct to 1 decimal place).

$$x = 60.3° \ (1 \ \text{d.p.})$$

Trigonometry

1 Find the sides marked with letters in each of the triangles below.

a)

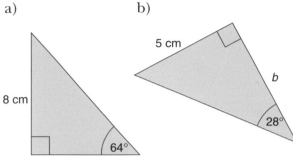

8 cm

64°

a

b)

5 cm

b

28°

c)

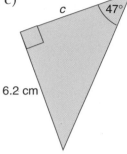

c

47°

6.2 cm

2 Find the angles marked with letters in each of the triangles below.

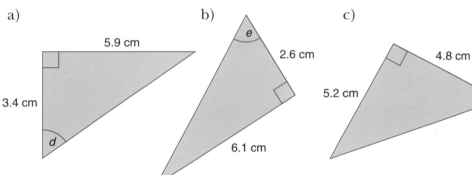

a)

5.9 cm

3.4 cm

d

b)

e

2.6 cm

6.1 cm

c)

4.8 cm

5.2 cm

f

3 Find the sides and angles marked with letters in each of the
triangles below. They are a mixture of the types you have met so far.

a)

3.2 cm

54°

p

b)

q

6.4 cm

6.7 cm

c)

r

25°

2.3 cm

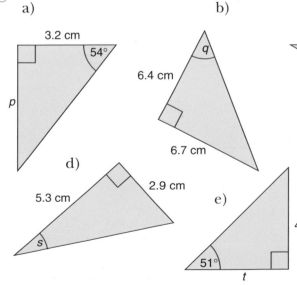

d)

2.9 cm

5.3 cm

s

e)

4.4 cm

51°

t

f)

3.8 cm

39°

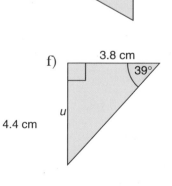

u

Using sine (sin)

In this triangle you can't use tan to find the opposite side, marked *x*, because you don't know the adjacent side.

You need to use another ratio.

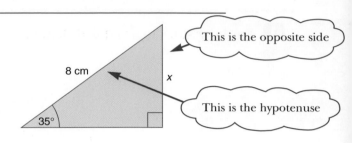

This is the opposite side

This is the hypotenuse

8 cm

x

35°

For a case like this, the ratio $\dfrac{\text{opposite}}{\text{hypotenuse}}$ is used.

This ratio is called **sine**, or **sin**. You will find a (sin) button on a scientific calculator. It is used in the same way as the (tan) button.

Use your calculator to find sin 90°. *Explain the answer you get.*

The examples below show how to use sin to find the opposite side, the hypotenuse or the angle.

Finding the opposite side using sine

$\sin 57° = \dfrac{\text{opp}}{\text{hyp}}$

$\sin 57° = \dfrac{x}{12}$

$x = 12 \times \sin 57°$

$x = 10.1 \ (3 \text{ s.f.})$

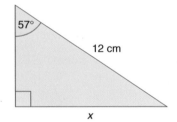

57°

12 cm

x

Finding the hypotenuse using sine

$\sin 29° = \dfrac{\text{opp}}{\text{hyp}}$

$\sin 29° = \dfrac{4.2}{x}$

$x \times \sin 29° = 4.2$

$x = 4.2 \div \sin 29°$

$x = 8.66 \ (3 \text{ s.f.})$

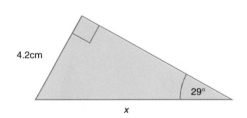

4.2cm

29°

x

Finding the angle using sine

Remember to use sin⁻¹ here

$\sin x = \dfrac{\text{opp}}{\text{hyp}}$

$\sin x = \dfrac{3.8}{6.1} = 0.623$

$x = 38.5° \ (3 \text{ s.f.})$

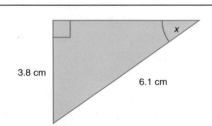

3.8 cm

6.1 cm

x

1 Find the sides marked with letters in each of these triangles.

a)

6.8 cm

a

41°

b)
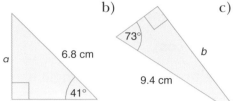

73°

b

9.4 cm

c)
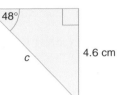

48°

c

4.6 cm

d)
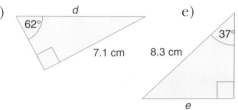

d

62°

7.1 cm

e)

8.3 cm

37°

e

f)
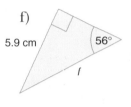

5.9 cm

56°

f

2 Find the angles marked with letters in each of these triangles.

a)

p

8.2 cm

6.3 cm

b)
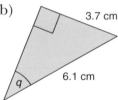

3.7 cm

q

6.1 cm

c)
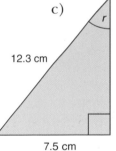

r

12.3 cm

7.5 cm

3 A ladder is 8 m long.

a) For safety reasons, the angle it makes with the ground should not be more than 75°.

What is the highest the ladder can reach?

b) What angle must it make with the ground to just reach a gutter 6 m above the ground?

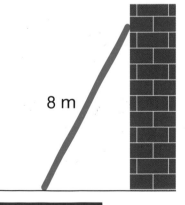

8 m

Find out what road gradients such as '1 in 10' mean. Use trigonometry to work out the angle of the slope for different gradients.

Using cosine (cos)

You have now met tangent, which links the opposite and adjacent sides, and sine, which links the opposite side and the hypotenuse. A way of linking the adjacent side and the hypotenuse is now needed.

The ratio $\dfrac{\text{adjacent}}{\text{hypotenuse}}$ is called the **cosine** (or **cos**).

It can be used to find the adjacent side, the hypotenuse or an angle in the same way that tangent and sine are used.

Use your calculator to find cos 90°. Explain the answer you get.

The examples below show how to use cos to find the opposite side, the hypotenuse or the angle.

Finding the adjacent side using cos

$$\cos 41° = \frac{\text{adj}}{\text{hyp}}$$

$$\cos 41° = \frac{x}{8}$$

$$x = 8 \times \cos 41°$$

$$x = 6.04 \text{ (3 s.f.)}$$

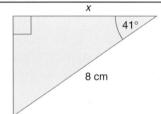

Finding the hypotenuse using cos

$$\cos 68° = \frac{\text{adj}}{\text{hyp}}$$

$$\cos 68° = \frac{7.5}{x}$$

$$x \times \cos 68° = 7.5$$

$$x = 7.5 \div \cos 68°$$

$$x = 20.0 \text{ (3 s.f.)}$$

Finding the angle using cos

Remember to use cos^{-1} here

$$\cos x = \frac{\text{adj}}{\text{hyp}}$$

$$\cos x = \frac{4.9}{8.3} = 0.590$$

$$x = 53.8°$$

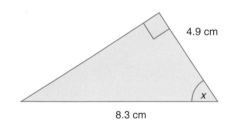

1 Find the sides marked with letters in each of the triangles below.

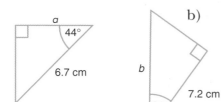

a)

44°

6.7 cm

a

b)

b

7.2 cm

31°

c)

4.6 cm

48°

c

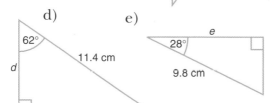

d)

62°

11.4 cm

d

e)

28°

e

9.8 cm

f)

53°

3.9 cm

f

2 Find the angles marked with letters in each of the triangles below.

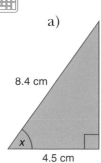

a)

8.4 cm

x

4.5 cm

b)

y

7.9 cm

6.6 cm

c)

5.2 cm

z

10.1 cm

3 A road slopes at 5° to the horizontal for 2 km measured
horizontally, as shown in the diagram below. How long is the road?

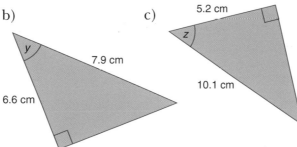

5°

2 km

Using sin, cos and tan

You have now met the three trigonometrical ratios. They are usually written in books or on formula sheets like this:

$$\sin \theta = \frac{\text{opp}}{\text{hyp}}$$

$$\cos \theta = \frac{\text{adj}}{\text{hyp}}$$

$$\tan \theta = \frac{\text{opp}}{\text{adj}}$$

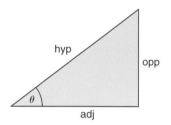

Some people remember these three ratios using the made-up word **SOHCAHTOA.**

Sin

  Opposite

    Hypotenuse

      Cos

        Adjacent

          Hypotenuse

            Tan

              Opposite

                Adjacent

When you want to find a missing side or angle in a right-angled triangle, the first thing to do is to decide whether to use sin, cos or tan. The example below shows how to do this.

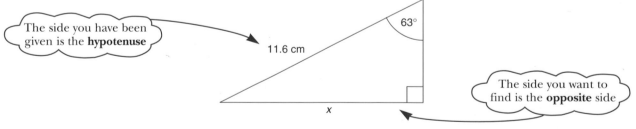

You need the ratio which involves **hypotenuse** and **opposite**. Look at the ratios at the top of the page and you will see that the one you need is sin.

$$\sin 63° = \frac{\text{opp}}{\text{hyp}}$$

$$\sin 63° = \frac{x}{11.6}$$

$$x = 11.6 \times \sin 63°$$

$$x = 10.3 \ (3 \text{ s.f.})$$

So the required side is 10.3 cm.

1 Find the sides marked with letters in these triangles.

a)
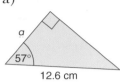
57°
a
12.6 cm

b)
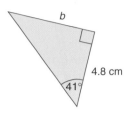
b
4.8 cm
41°

c)
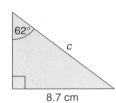
62°
c
8.7 cm

d)
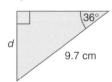
36°
d
9.7 cm

e)
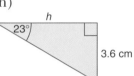
e
28°
7.5 cm

f)
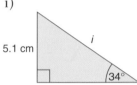
f
55°
6.9 cm

g)

g
42°
4.3 cm

h)
h
23°
3.6 cm

i)
5.1 cm
i
34°

2 Find the angles marked with letters in these triangles.

a)
4.8 cm
p
6.5 cm

b)
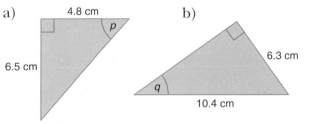
6.3 cm
q
10.4 cm

c)
6.7 cm
5.2 cm
r

d)
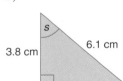
s
3.8 cm
6.1 cm

e)
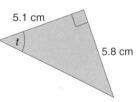
5.1 cm
t
5.8 cm

f)
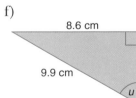
8.6 cm
9.9 cm
u

Using trigonometry

Trigonometry can be used to solve real-life problems. Always start by drawing a clear diagram showing the right-angled triangle that you are using.

Example 1

Anna is going to climb a hill which is 1400 m high. She measures the length of the climb on a map and finds that it is 6.5 km.

What is the angle of the slope?

Solution

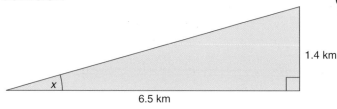

> The length of the climb must be the horizontal distance as it has been measured on a map.

1.4 km

6.5 km

The two sides marked are the **opposite** and the **adjacent**. So you need to use **tangent** to find the angle.

$$\tan x = \frac{1.4}{6.5} \qquad x = 12.2°$$

The angle of the slope is 12.2°.

Do you think the slope is really 12.2° all the way up the hill?

Example 2

A ship sails 50 km on a bearing of 140°. How far south and how far east is it from its starting point?

Solution

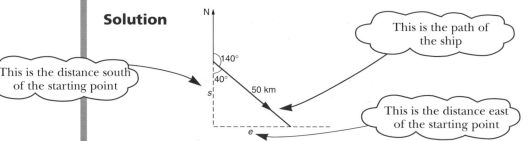

> This is the path of the ship

N

140°

40°

s

50 km

> This is the distance south of the starting point

> This is the distance east of the starting point

e

The side marked *s* is the **adjacent** side, and the side marked 50 km is the **hypotenuse**. So you need to use **cosine** to find *s*.

$$\cos 40° = \frac{\text{adj}}{\text{hyp}} \qquad \cos 40° = \frac{s}{50}$$
$$s = 50 \times \cos 40° = 38.3$$

The ship is 38.3 km south of its starting point.

Which trig ratio would you use to work out e?

1 a) An aeroplane flies 300 km on a bearing of 245°. How far south and how far west is it from its starting point?

b) An aeroplane flies 550 km on a bearing of 318°. How far north and how far west is it from its starting point?

2 A sailor in a small boat can see a cliff in the distance which he knows is 150 m high. The angle of elevation of the top of the cliff is 8°. How far is the boat from the foot of the cliff?

3 a) A path up a hill slopes at 15°. The path is 3.6 km long. How high is the hill?

b) Another path up the other side of the same hill is 4.3 km long. What is the angle of the slope of this path?

4 The guy ropes for a tent run from the top of the tent pole, which is 1.5 metres tall, to a point on the ground near the tent. Each rope should ideally be at 45° to the ground.

a) How long should each guy rope be?

b) How far will each rope be from the base of the tent pole?

5 A short flight of steps, 1.2 m high, is to be replaced by a ramp. The slope of the ramp must not be more than 10°. What is the shortest the ramp could be?

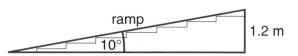

6 a) A ship starts from point A and sails 200 km on a bearing of 115° until it reaches point B. How far south and how far east is it from point A?

b) The ship then sails a further 150 km from point B on a bearing of 230° until it reaches point C. How far south and how far west is it from point B?

c) How far south and how far east is the ship now from point A?

d) What bearing must the ship sail on to get back to point A directly from point C?

Finishing off

Now that you have finished this chapter you should be able to

★ find sides and angles in right-angled triangles using sine, cosine and tangent

★ use trigonometry to solve problems involving right-angled triangles.

Use the questions in the next exercise to check that you understand everything.

Mixed exercise

1 Find the sides and angles marked with letters in the triangles below.

a)

a

61°

4.8 cm

b)

48°

6.3 cm

b

c)

5.9 cm

9.4 cm

c

d)

8.1 cm

42°

d

e)

7.3 cm

35°

e

f)

f

6.9 cm

4.5 cm

g)

11.7 cm

g

71°

h)

5.1 cm

h

10.6 cm

i)

56°

9.3 cm

i

j)

5.8 cm

j

8.8 cm

2 The diagram shows a beam of light from a spotlight in a concert hall 5.4 m high.

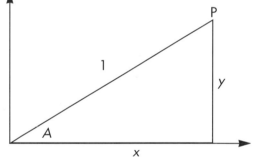

a) Find the radius of the circle of light on the floor.

b) Find the area of the circle of light.

3 Simon and Sue set out from a Youth Hostel for a country walk.

They walk 3 km on a bearing of 285°.

a) How far north and how far west are they from the Youth Hostel?

b) They then walk 2 km due north. Find the bearing they need to walk on to get back to the Youth Hostel.

Investigation

Look at the triangle in this diagram.

$\dfrac{x}{1} = \cos A$ so $x = \cos A$

$\dfrac{y}{1} = \sin A$ so $y = \sin A$

The point P has co-ordinates $(\cos A, \sin A)$.

What happens if angle A is greater than 90°?

Use your calculator to find $\sin A$ and $\cos A$.

Copy and complete this table for angles at 10° intervals up to 360°.

angle A	sin A	cos A
0°	0	1
10°	0.17	0.98
20°	0.34	0.94
30°		

Plot the graph of:

sin A against A

cos A against A

What do you notice?

Seven

Inequalities

Before you start this chapter you should be able to

★ expand brackets

★ solve simple linear equations

★ draw graphs of straight lines from their equations.

Using inequalities

Look at these notices.

They all describe restrictions on ages, heights and prices.

These restrictions can be written as **inequalities** using special symbols.

< means *is less than*

> means *is greater than*

≤ means *is less than or equal to*

≥ means *is greater than or equal to*

Read 4 < 7 as *4 is less than 7*

Read 3 > 1 as *3 is greater than 1*

Read $p ≥ 5$ as *p is greater than or equal to 5*

Let y stand for age in years. Then

$y ≥ 15$ describes the age of person who can go to the film *Wilde*.

$y < 16$ describes the age of a person whose Cinderella ticket will cost £2.50.

 Write inequalities, using the symbols, for the restrictions in the other notices.

What other restrictions are commonly shown in notices and signs?

You have already met the inequality symbols in Chapter 4, when you were grouping data. In this chapter you will learn about other ways to use them.

 What is the other way of writing 7 > 4 ?

1 Write these statements as inequalities.

a) *x* is greater than 3   b) *x* is greater than or equal to zero

c) *x* is less than 5   d) *x* is less than or equal to –2.

2 Write these inequalities in words.

a) $x < 8$ b) $p > 100$ c) $q \geq 100$

d) $y < 17$ e) $x \leq 20$ f) $b \geq -3$

3 For each of these, copy the numbers down in the same order, replacing the comma by an inequality sign (< or >).

a) 2, 9   b) 13, 3   c) –3, –13

d) 13, –3 e) 3.8, 3.3 f) 0.5, 0.625

4 Look at each of these signs and write down the restriction shown using the inequality symbols. (Choose a suitable letter, in each case, to stand for the quantity that is being restricted.)

a)

b)

c)

Old Man Theatre

Party rates for groups of 20 or more

d)

LIFT
MAX LOAD
5 PERSONS

e)

Holidays in Spain

7 nights – less than £250

f)

MATCHES

Min. contents 50

g)

Narrow Bridge
►2·5 m◄

h)

RAINBOW
Building
Society
HIGH INTEREST ACCOUNT
Minimum deposit £500

5 You can write an inequality in two ways.

For example, $9 > 7$ could be written as $7 < 9$.

Write down each of your inequalities from question 3 in another way.

Number lines

It is often helpful to show an inequality on a number line.

This is how you show the inequality $x > 4$.

> The empty circle shows that x *cannot* be equal to 4

> Any number to the right of 4 is greater than 4

This is how you show $x \leq 2$.

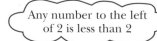

> The solid circle shows that x *can* be equal to 2

> Any number to the left of 2 is less than 2

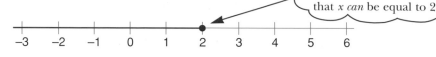

 Think of some possible values for x for each inequality and check that they come on the marked part of the number line.

Is –4 greater than 1 or less than 1?

Combining inequalities

'Young Singles' is a club for people in their twenties and thirties. The inequalities which describe the ages of its members are

$$y \geq 20 \quad \text{and} \quad y < 40.$$

As y is *between* 20 and 40 you can combine these and write $20 \leq y < 40$.

You can show it on a number line like this.

> People who have had their 20th birthday are included

> People who have had their 40th birthday are not included

 Write a similar inequality for the age of a student at your school or college.

Penny is 1.6 m tall (correct to 1 decimal place).

Write an inequality to show exactly what this means, and show it on a number line.

To qualify for cheap rail tickets you must be under 16, or else 60 or over. Your age has to satisfy the inequality

$$x < 16 \quad \text{or} \quad x \geq 60.$$

You can show it on a number line like this.

 The number x has a square that is greater than 9. Where can x lie on the number line?

1 Show each of these inequalities on a number line.

a) $x \geq 2$ b) $x > -1$ c) $x < 8$

d) $x \leq 2$ e) $x < 0$ f) x is positive

g) x is not more than 12   h) x is at least 6   i) x is not positive

2 A second class stamp can be used to send a letter weighing no more than 60 g.

a) Write this as an inequality for w, the weight of the letter in grams.
b) Show your answer on a number line.

3 Show these measurements on a number line.

a) 3.8 m (correct to 1 d.p.)   b) 2.0 kg (correct to 1 d.p.)

c) 5 m (to the nearest metre).   d) 3000 m (to the nearest 1000 m)

e) 3000 m (to the nearest 100 m)   f) 0.16 kg (correct to 2 d.p.)

4 Combine the inequalities and show the results on a number line

a) $x \geq 3$ and $x \leq 7$ b) $x \leq 5$ and $x \geq -2$ c) $x < 0$ and $x \geq -4$

d) $y \geq 1.65$ and $y < 1.75$ e) $a > -1$ and $a \leq 0$ f) $b < -3$ and $b > -6$

g) $x \geq -1$ and $x \geq 2$ (Be careful!)   h) $c \leq 7$ and $c \leq 2$

5 You join the queue at the supermarket checkout with this sign.

Write down an inequality for the number of items, x, in your basket.

Write down all the possible values of x and mark these points on a number line.

EXPRESS CHECKOUT

FEWER THAN

10 ITEMS

6 a) Copy and complete this table.

x	-4	-3	-2	-1	0	1	2	3	4
x^2		9		1			4		

b) Show each of these on a number line, using your table to help you.

(i) $x^2 \leq 16$ (ii) $x^2 \geq 9$ (iii) $x^2 < 25$ (iv) $x^2 > 1$

Write the inequalities shown on the number lines below in a similar way.

c)   d)

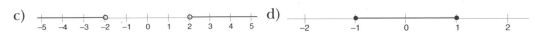

Inequality signs are used to show the class limits in the table on page 44. Draw a number line to show the range of possible values for an item in each class. Use a different colour for each one.

What do you notice?

Solving inequalities

For what values of x is $3x - 5 > 16$?

You can solve this inequality in just the same way as you solve an equation.

An equation

$$3x - 5 = 16$$

$$3x - 5 > 16$$

An inequality

Add 5 to both sides $3x = 21$ $3x > 21$

Divide both sides by 3 $x = 7$ $x > 7$

This is the solution of the inequality. It means that x can have any value greater than 7.

The equation has just one solution

Check using a number just greater than 7

Check: When $x = 7$ When $x = 8$

$$3x - 5 = 21 - 5 = 16 ✓   3x - 5 = 24 - 5 = 19 ✓$$

The inequality holds because 19 > 16

Check for yourself that when $x = 6$ the inequality is not true.

Find the value of the expression $3x - 5$ when $x = 10$ and when $x = 7.5$.

What do you think will happen when $x = 2$?

You can do what you like to an equation, so long as you do the same to both sides. You can add or subtract any number, and you can multiply or divide by any number.

Look at the inequality 30 > 20. You know that it is valid.

Show that it is still valid if you add, subtract, multiply by or divide by 5.

Show that it is no longer valid when you multiply or divide by –5.

What happens to the inequality sign?

> **You solve inequalities just as you solve equations, except that if you multiply or divide by a negative number you must reverse the inequality sign.**

Example

Solve $-2x > 8$

Solution $-2x > 8$

Divide by –2 $x < -4$

Check: when $x = -5$, $-2x = (-2) \times (-5) = 10$ ✓

Another way to do this is to add $2x$ to both sides then subtract 8 from both sides. Try this to check you get the same answer.

1 Solve these inequalities.

a) $x + 1 < 7$ b) $2x + 1 \le 11$

c) $x - 3 \ge 5$ d) $3x - 2 \ge 10$

e) $x - 4 < -1$ f) $2x + 17 > 29$

g) $5x - 2 \le 16$ h) $2x + 11 \le 5$

i) $3 + 4x > 11$ j) $5 - x \ge 3$

k) $7 - 2x \le 1$ l) $14 \le 5 - 3x$

2 Find all the possible values of y when

a) $y < 20$ and y is a prime number

b) $20 \le y \le 40$ and y is a square number

c) $3 < y < 12$ and y is a factor of 12

d) $12 > y > 3$ and y is a multiple of 3.

3 Last Saturday Grandad went to the races. He placed a bet of £x on the first race and his horse came in first at 5 to 1. Grandad won £$5x$. After that he lost £200 of his winnings.

a) Write an expression for the winnings he had left.

b) This amount was still more than he had bet on the first horse.

Write this as an inequality and solve it for x.

4 Ben looks at the weight card his mother has kept from when he was a baby. He finds that he now weighs 52 kg more than he did when he was born. This is more than 14 times his birthweight.

Write this as an inequality for w, his birthweight, and solve it.

5 Solve these inequalities.

a) $2x + 5 \ge x + 16$ b) $4x - 3 \ge x + 3$ c) $8 < x + 1$

d) $2(x + 4) < 20$ e) $4 \le x + 3 \le 11$ f) $20 \ge 2x > 6$

g) $13 < 2x < 19$ h) $0 \le x - 2 \le 18$ i) $5 < 2x + 1 \le 23$

j) $3(x - 2) > 2x + 5$ k) $10(x - 4) \ge 5(x + 8)$ l) $2 - x > 3 - 2x$

Choose an inequality for x, such as $x < 5$ or $x \ge 1$.

Multiply both sides by the same number.

Add or subtract the same number on both sides.

You now have an inequality for a partner to solve.

Write it on another piece of paper so your working is not visible.

See if your partner can solve the inequality and get back to your starting point.

Inequalities and graphs

Look at this chart showing people's heights and weights.

If you plot your height and weight on it you can see whether you are overweight, underweight or about right for your height.

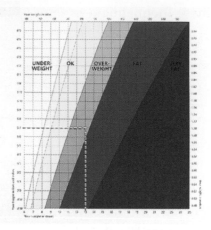

In this situation you are content if the point you plot is in the central **region** of the graph. You do not need it to be on a particular line.

You can often describe regions of a graph using inequalities. In this chapter you will learn how to use inequalities to describe some regions, and how to show on a graph the region described by one or more inequalities.

Look at this graph. It shows the region for which

$$0 \leq y \leq 3 \text{ and } 0 \leq x \leq 5.$$

All points in the shaded region have x and y values that satisfy these inequalities.

 Check that this is true for point A.

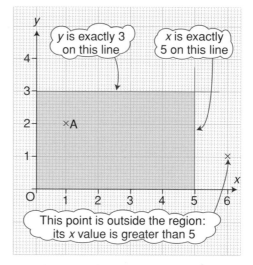

This graph shows the region for which

$$3 < x \leq 5 \text{ and } y \geq 1.$$

 Is point P inside the region? Explain your answer.

 Sketch a graph showing the region for which $3 < x \leq 5$ and $y \leq 0$.

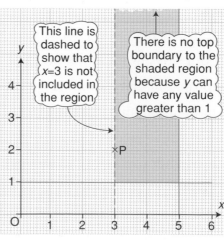

1 Write down the inequalities represented by the shaded regions.

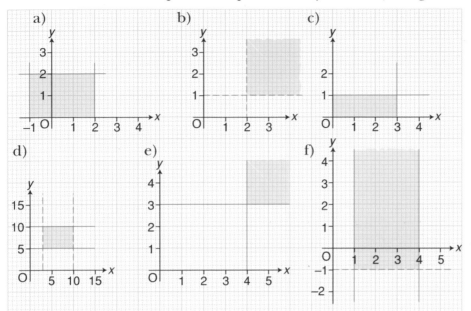

2 Sketch graphs and shade the regions that represent these inequalities.

a) $0 \le x \le 4$
   $0 \le y \le 8$

b) $-1 \le x \le 3$
   $2 < y < 4$

c) $x \ge 2$
   $y > 1$

d) $x < 2$
   $0 \le y < 4$

e) $30 \le x < 50$
   $20 \le y < 40$

f) $x \ge 1$
   $y \le 5$

3 In a hot air balloon race the winners were in the air for 2 hours and went a distance of 100 miles. They went furthest and were in the air for the longest time.

The shortest distance travelled by any of the balloons was 5 miles and the shortest time in the air was 20 minutes.

a) Write down suitable inequalities for the time taken and the distance travelled by the competitors in the race.

b) Illustrate these inequalities on a graph and shade the region in which all the balloons' times and distances could be plotted.

Regions bounded by sloping lines

So far you have met regions of a graph **bounded** by horizontal and vertical lines, but regions can be bounded by sloping lines.

Look at this graph of

$$y = x + 1$$

The red points are above the line and the blue ones are below it.

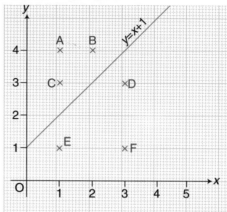

 For each point, write down the co-ordinates (x, y), then write an inequality of the form $y > x + 1$ or $y < x + 1$. What do you notice?

Example

Draw the graph of $x + y = 10$.

Shade the region in which

$$x + y \leq 10, \quad y \geq 0 \text{ and } x \geq 0.$$

Solution

Make a table of values for $x + y = 10$.

x	0	10	5
y	10	0	5

> For equations of this form it is easiest to work out the x and y values when $x = 0$ and when $y = 0$, then at one other point (as a check).

> Test point at $(1,1)$: $x + y = 2$
> On this side of the line, $x + y < 10$

 Which region would you shade for $x + y \leq 10$, $x \geq 0$ and $y \leq 0$?

Which region would you shade for $x + y \leq 10$, $x \leq 0$ and $y \leq 0$?

1 a) Draw a graph of the line $x + y = 6$ for values of x and y from 0 to 7.

  b) Mark these points on your graph:

   A(3, 6), B(5, 5), C(6, 2), D(1, 3), E(2, 2) and F(4, 1).

  c) Find the value of $x + y$ at each of the points A to F.

  d) Shade the region of your graph where $x + y \leq 6$.

2 a) Draw a graph of the line $y = 2x + 2$ for values of x from 0 to 5 and of y from 0 to 12.

  b) Mark these points on your graph:

   P(0, 4), Q(2, 8), R(3, 9), S(2, 1), T(5, 1).

  c) Find the value of $2x + 2$ at each of points P to T.

  d) Shade the region of your graph where $y \leq 2x + 2$.

3 a) Draw a graph of the line $y = x$ for values of x and y from 0 to 5. (Use a dashed line.)

  b) Draw on your graph the line $y = 4$ (again dashed, not solid).

  c) By using test points, find the region of your graph where $y > x$ and $y < 4$.

  d) Why was it important to use dashed lines?

4 Sanjay is making a table. He has a carved strip 500 cm long that he wants to put round the edge of the table. The table is to be rectangular, of width x and length y cms.

  a) Write down an expression for the perimeter of the table in terms of x and y.

  b) Explain why $2x + 2y \leq 500$ and write this inequality in its simplest form.

  c) Sanjay wants the table to be more than 80 cm wide. Write this as an inequality.

  d) Draw a graph and shade the feasible region for the dimensions of the table.

5 For each of these, draw a graph and shade the region represented by the inequalities.

  a) $0 < x < 6$, $3 < y < 6$ b) $0 \leq x \leq 4$, $2 \leq y \leq 6$, $x \geq y$

  c) $x + y \geq 4$, $0 \leq x \leq 8$, $0 \leq y \leq 10$ d) $y < x + 3$, $y \geq 0$, $1 < x < 5$

Solution sets

Jackie has a £12 gift token to spend. She wants to use it to buy more mugs and plates like these for her bedsit.

 Find a combination of mugs and plates that costs exactly £12.

Find a combination that costs less than £12.

Jackie can buy any combination that costs up to £12.

You can write this as an inequality:

> *x* is the number of mugs.
> 3*x* is their cost in pounds.

$$3x + 2y \leq 12$$

> *y* is the number of plates.
> 2*y* is their cost in pounds.

 The numbers x and y must be integers in this problem. Why?

You can show the solutions to this inequality on a graph. You start by drawing the line

$$3x + 2y = 12$$

Then use a test point to decide on which side of the line $3x + 2y \leq 12$.

The blue crosses show all the combinations that Jackie can buy. These points make up the **solution set**

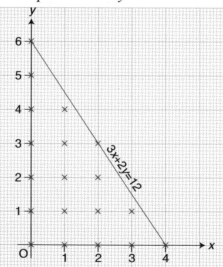

 Why are none of the points to the right of the line?

Why is it not correct to shade the whole region to the left of the line in this case?

Points on the x and y axes are included in the solution. Why?

Points for which x or y is negative are not included. Why not?

Three of the points in the solution set lie on the line $3x + 2y = 12$. What is special about these points?

94

1 a) Draw a graph of $x + 3y = 9$ for $0 \leq x \leq 10$ and $0 \leq y \leq 4$.

b) Find the points $(1, 2)$ and $(2, 4)$ and work out the value of $x + 3y$ at each of these points.

c) Shade the region where $x + 3y \leq 9$.

d) Mark the set of points where x and y are both positive integers and where $x + 3y \leq 9$.

2 Kim is a gymnast. She has to train for at least 10 hours a week.

There are two training sessions on a Saturday, each 4 hours long, and the weekday sessions are 2 hours each evening. There is no training on Sundays.

a) Using w for the number of weekday sessions and s for the number of Saturday sessions that Kim attends in a week, write an inequality for w and s.

b) Clearly Kim cannot attend more than 5 weekday sessions in a week. Write this as an inequality for w.

c) Write a similar inequality for s.

d) Show all the possible combinations of s and w on a graph.

3 Dean works for x hours during the week and y hours at the weekend. He cannot work for more than 21 hours per week because he is at college.

a) Write down an inequality to show this.

b) Dean earns £4 per hour during the week and £7 per hour at weekends. He aims to earn at least enough to pay his rent of £56 a week. The shifts he works are always whole numbers of hours.

Write down a second inequality to show this.

c) Draw a suitable graph and mark on it the points in the solution set.

d) Dean tries to do as much weekend work as possible because it pays better. He is told that the number of weekend hours must not be more than the number of weekday hours.

Add the line $y = x$ to your graph.

e) Using algebra, find the co-ordinates of the point where $y = x$ crosses $x + y = 21$.

f) Find the maximum amount Dean can earn in a week.

Finishing off

> **Now that you have finished this chapter you should**
>
> ★ understand the symbols $<$, $>$, $\leq$, $\geq$
>
> ★ be able to represent an inequality on a number line
>
> ★ be able to solve an inequality using algebra
>
> ★ be able to represent inequalities for x and y by shading areas or marking sets of points on a graph.

Use the following questions to check that you understand everything.

Mixed exercise

1 Write each of these inequalities in words and show it on a number line.

a) $x > 2$ b) $x \leq 1$ c) $x \geq 4$

d) $x < -3$ e) $-2 < x < 3$ f) $1 \leq x \leq 5$

2 Write the age ranges in these lonely hearts' advertisements as inequalities. Show each one on a number line.

> ● **M 5' 9"** dark, lively personality, likes jazz and dancing, Seeks F 20–35, for friendship and outings.
>
> ● **F** professional, young 36 seeks M 30s for companionship/romance.

● M
S
fo

3 Madeleine has inherited some money from her aunt.

She puts it in one of these accounts.

It is earning 5.70% annual interest.

Write an inequality for the sum, £m, that Madeleine inherited.

RAINBOW Building Society

SAVINGS RATES

Balance	Annual Interest
£1 – £4,999	5·35%
£5,000 – £9,999	5·70%
£10,000 – £24,999	6·20%
£25,000 – £49,999	6·50%
£50,000 – £99,999	6·70%
£100,000 +	6·80%

4 Solve these inequalities.

a) $x + 3 \leq 8$

b) $2x - 5 \geq 21$

c) $2x + 1 > x + 9$

d) $5(x + 11) < 80$

e) $2(2x - 3) \leq 3x + 2$

f) $-3 < x + 1$

g) $4(x + 2) - 3(x + 1) > 12$

h) $x^2 \geq 25$

i) $x^2 \leq 4$

5 Write down the inequalities represented by the shaded areas.

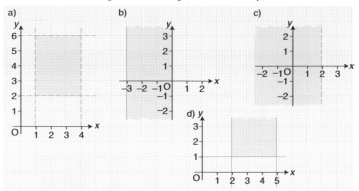

a) b) c) d)

6 Draw suitable graphs and shade the regions that represent the following inequalities.

a) $1 \le x \le 6$
$-1 \le y \le 5$
$x \le y$

b) $x + y \le 10$
$x \ge 0$
$y \ge 0$

c) $y > x + 2$
$0 \le x \le 5$
$y < 9$

d) $y \ge 0$
$x \ge 1$
$y \ge 2x$

e) $-2 \le x \le 2$
$-3 \le y \le 2$
$x + y \le 0$

f) $x^2 \le 9$
$0 < y < 5$
$y > 2x + 1$

7 In a pub quiz, a team scores 10 points for a correct answer to a starter question. If they get the starter question right, they are asked a bonus question worth a further 5 points.

a) How many points does a team score when it gets 30 starter questions and 19 bonus questions right?

b) Write down an expression for the score when the team gets x starter questions and y bonus questions right.

c) Last season James's team's highest score was 430 points.

Write down an inequality that is true for each of his team's scores last season.

d) Explain why $x \ge 0$, $y \ge 0$ and $x \ge y$.

e) Draw a graph to illustrate the inequalities in c) and d) and show where you could mark the points in the solution set.

8 a) Draw a graph of the line $3x + 4y = 60$.

b) On the same axes, draw the line $x + y = 17$.

c) Shade the region in which

$x \ge 0$, $y \ge 0$, $3x + 4y \le 60$ and $x + y \ge 17$.

d) Write down the co-ordinates of the vertices of your shaded triangle.

Eight

Indices and standard form

Before you start this chapter you should be able to

★ use simple index notation, such as 4^3, 2^5, . . .

★ find squares, cubes and higher powers

★ find square roots and cube roots

★ multiply and divide numbers by powers of 10 without using a calculator

★ work out the value of a large number given in standard form on a calculator display.

Reminder

Multiplying by 10 moves the decimal point one place to the right.

$$4.5 \times 10 = 45$$

Dividing by 10 moves the decimal point one place to the left.

$$243 \div 10 = 24.3$$

8.5 12

A display like this (or similar to it) means 8.5×10^{12} which is 8 500 000 000 000

Revision exercise

1 Work out the value of

a) 2^3 b) 6^2 c) 3^4 d) 2^6 e) 3^5 f) 4^4 g) 11^2 h) 1.5^3

2 Work out the value of

a) 9^2 b) $\sqrt{81}$ c) 5^3 d) $\sqrt[3]{125}$

e) 20^3 f) $\sqrt{49}$ g) $\sqrt[3]{1000}$ h) 400^2

3 Jody packs sugar cubes in boxes like this.

a) How many are there on the top layer?

b) How many are there in the box?

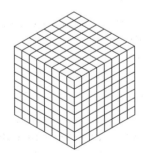

4 Steven is designing a garden. He has 200 square slabs. He uses all these slabs to make two identical square patios.

a) How many slabs are there along an edge of one of these patios?

Steven decides that he would rather have one large patio.

b) What size is the largest square patio that he can make?

c) How many slabs are left over?

5 Work out

a) 52×10 b) $83 \div 10$ c) $6.9 \div 10$ d) 23×100

e) $47 \div 100$ f) 6.4×10 g) 0.7×10 h) $528 \div 100$

i) 93.45×100 j) 0.8×10 k) $9.12 \div 10$ l) 573×1000

m) $7.5 \div 100$ n) $39\,371 \div 100$ o) 14.065×10 p) $105\,600 \div 10$

6 Work out the value of the numbers displayed here.

a)

b)

Investigation

Copy and complete this table.

$2^1 = 2$	$4^1 =$	$6^1 =$	$8^1 = 8$
$2^2 =$	$4^2 =$	$6^2 = 36$	$8^2 =$
$2^3 =$	$4^3 = 64$	$6^3 =$	$8^3 =$
$2^4 = 16$	$4^4 =$	$6^4 =$	$8^4 = 4096$
$2^5 =$	$4^5 =$	$6^5 = 7776$	$8^5 =$

Look at the pattern of last digits of the numbers in each column.

(i)   What do you think the last digit is for each number to the power 6?

(ii) Write down what you think the last digit is in each of these numbers.

a) 4^9 b) 6^8 c) 2^{11} d) 8^7 e) 2^9 f) 8^{10}

Check that you can use your calculator to find cube roots.

Rules of indices

Look at this table.

$\div 2$	$16 = 2 \times 2 \times 2 \times 2$	2^4	$\div 2$
$\div 2$	$8 = 2 \times 2 \times 2$	2^3	$\div 2$
$\div 2$	$4 = 2 \times 2$	2^2	$\div 2$
$\div 2$	$2 = 2$	2^1	$\div 2$
$\div 2$	$1 = 1$	2^0	$\div 2$
$\div 2$	$\dfrac{1}{2} = \dfrac{1}{2}$	2^{-1}	$\div 2$
$\div 2$	$\dfrac{1}{4} = \dfrac{1}{2 \times 2} = \dfrac{1}{2^2}$	2^{-2}	$\div 2$
	$\dfrac{1}{8} = \dfrac{1}{2 \times 2 \times 2} = \dfrac{1}{2^3}$	2^{-3}	

You can see the meaning of 2 to the power zero and to a negative power. Notice that

$$2^0 = 1 \qquad \text{and} \qquad 2^{-3} = \frac{1}{2^3}$$

 What are the values of 10^0 and 10^{-2}?

When you write 16 as 2^4 then 2^4 is called **index form**

When you multiply two numbers given in index form you add the powers.

$$2^4 \times 2^3 = 2^{4+3} = 2^7$$

$2^4 \times 2^3 = (2 \times 2 \times 2 \times 2) \times (2 \times 2 \times 2) = 2^7$

 What is $2^2 \times 2^3 \times 2^4$?

When you divide one number by another you subtract the powers.

$$2^5 \div 2^3 = 2^{5-3} = 2^2$$

$\dfrac{2^5}{2^3} = \dfrac{2 \times 2 \times 2 \times 2 \times 2}{2 \times 2 \times 2} = 2 \times 2 = 2^2$

 What is $2^4 \div 2$? (Hint: 2 is the same as 2^1).

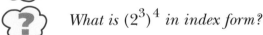 *What is $(2^3)^4$ in index form?*

You can write the rules on this page as general laws.

$$a^0 = 1 \qquad\qquad\qquad a^{-n} = \frac{1}{a^n}$$

$$a^m \times a^n = a^{m+n} \qquad\qquad a^m \div a^n = a^{m-n}$$

1 Write each value as a fraction. For example $2^{-2} = \dfrac{1}{4}$

a) 4^{-2} b) 10^{-3} c) 5^{-2} d) 8^{-1} e) 3^{-3} f) 6^{-2}

g) 10^{-2} h) 3^{-4} i) 4^{-1} j) 2^{-4} k) 6^{-3} l) 10^{-4}

2 Work out the value of

a) 7^2 b) 3^{-2} c) 10^{-1} d) 4^3 e) 9^{-2} f) 6^0

g) 2^5 h) 5^{-3} i) 10^6 j) 9^1 k) 5^{-1} l) 7^0

m) 6^3 n) 8^{-2} o) 4^1 p) 5^4

3 Work these out giving your answer in index form.

For example $4^3 \times 4^2 = 4^5$

a) $5^2 \times 5^4$ b) $2^6 \times 2^3 \times 2^2$ c) 6×6^3 d) $10^6 \div 10^3$

e) $2^8 \div 2$ f) $(10^2)^3$ g) $(3^4)^2$ h) $4^5 \times 4^{-3}$

i) $10^3 \div 10^{-1}$ j) $(5^{-1})^2$ k) $3^4 \times 3^{-2} \times 3$ l) $2^{-1} \div 2^{-2}$

m) $\dfrac{4^9}{4^3 \times 4^4}$ n) $\dfrac{3^4 \times 3^2}{3^8}$ o) $\dfrac{(2^3)^2 \times 2}{2^7}$ p) $\dfrac{10^4 \times 10^6 \times 10}{10^5 \times 10^3}$

Investigation

1 Use your calculator to work out

a) 7×10

b) $7 \times 10 \times 10$

c) $7 \times 10 \times 10 \times 10$

. . . and so on until you get an answer in standard form.

How many digits can your calculator display?

2 Use your calculator to work out

a) $7 \div 10$

b) $7 \div 10 \div 10$

c) $7 \div 10 \div 10 \div 10$

. . . until the form of answer changes.

For which calculation does the form of your answer change?

What does the display show?

What do you think this display means?

Standard form

Large numbers

The speed of light is 300 000 000 m/s.

Large numbers like this are rather untidy.

300 000 000 is the same as

$$3 \times 100\ 000\ 000$$

$$\text{or } 3 \times 10 \times 10 \times 10 \times 10 \times 10 \times 10 \times 10 \times 10$$

This can be written as 3×10^8.

This is an example of **standard form**. The leading number, 2, is between 1 and 10.

The speed of sound in standard form is 3.3×10^2 m/s.

What is 3.3×10^2 in decimal form?

$$3.3 \times 10^2 = 3.3 \times 10 \times 10 = 330$$

Small numbers

The wavelength of yellow light is 0.000 000 6 metres.

Small numbers like this are also untidy.

$$0.000\ 000\ 6 = \frac{6}{10\ 000\ 000} \text{ or } \frac{6}{10 \times 10 \times 10 \times 10 \times 10 \times 10 \times 10}$$

This can be written as $\frac{6}{10^7}$ or 6×10^{-7}. ← This is in standard form.

The wavelength of mercury green light is 5.4×10^{-7} m.

$$5.4 \times 10^{-7} = \frac{5.4}{10^7} = \frac{5.4}{10 \times 10 \times 10 \times 10 \times 10 \times 10 \times 10} = 0.000\ 000\ 54$$

The wavelength of mercury green light is 0.000 000 54 m.

This number, 0.000 000 54, can also be written as 54×10^{-8}.

This is not in standard form because the leading number, 54, is not between 1 and 10. You can convert it like this

$$54 \times 10^{-8} = 5.4 \times 10 \times 10^{-8} \quad \text{(because } 54 = 5.4 \times 10\text{)}$$

$$= 5.4 \times 10^{-7} \quad \text{(because } 10 \times 10^{-8} = 10^{-7}\text{)}$$

1 These numbers are in standard form.

Write them out in full.

a) 6×10^2 b) 3×10^4 c) 7×10^{-3} d) 4×10^{-5}

e) 4.5×10^6 f) 5.4×10^{-3} g) 9.4×10^3 h) 8.75×10^{-4}

i) 1.6×10^{-2} j) 2.75×10^6 k) 8.3×10^{-5} l) 1.05×10^4

m) 7.3×10^3 n) 8×10^{-9} o) 4×10^{-1} p) 8.25×10^{10}

2 Write these numbers in standard form.

a) 4000   b) 800 000   c) 0.003   d) 0.0009

e) 26 000   f) 0.025   g) 7 500 000   h) 0.000 037

i) 810   j) 0.005 43   k) 0.93   l) 64 000

m) 0.016   n) 147 000 000   o) 0.507   p) 9040

3 Alison is using this spreadsheet for her science assignment.

	D	E	F
1	637 983	5E–03	4.38E+09
2	7.25E–04	9.42E+08	694
3	4.6E+12	83 926	7.5E–06

Large and small numbers are displayed using an E.

So in D2, 7.25E–04 means 7.25×10^{-4}.

Work out the value of the entry in

a) E1   b) D3   c) E2   d) F3

4 This table shows the approximate diameter of each planet.

Planet	Diameter (m)
Mercury	4.88×10^6
Venus	1.21×10^7
Earth	1.28×10^7
Mars	6.79×10^6
Jupiter	1.44×10^8
Saturn	1.21×10^8
Uranus	5.08×10^7
Neptune	4.95×10^7
Pluto	2.30×10^6

Arrange them in order of size.

The population of Sweden is about 8 800 000 or 8.8×10^6.

Find out the approximate population of nine other countries.

Present your results in a table, showing the populations in both standard form and as ordinary numbers.

Calculations using standard form

This diagram shows the distances of the planets from the Sun.

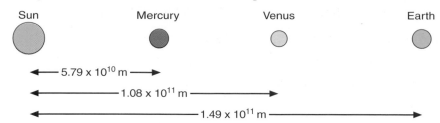

How far is Earth from Mercury when they are at their closest?

It is $(1.49 \times 10^{11} - 5.79 \times 10^{10})$ metres.

You work it out on your calculator like this.

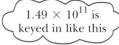
1.49 × 10¹¹ is keyed in like this

5.79 × 10¹⁰ is keyed in like this

Earth is 9.11×10^{10} m from Mercury when they are at their closest.

The volume of the Earth is 1.08×10^{21} m^3.

Each cubic metre has, on average a mass of 5.52×10^3 kg.

Earth has a **density** of 5.52×10^3 kg/m^3

What is the mass of the Earth?

mass = volume × density

$$= (1.08 \times 10^{21}) \times (5.52 \times 10^3)$$

Work this out on your calculator. Check you get 5.96×10^{24}.

The mass of the Earth is 5.96×10^{24} kg.

5.96×10^{24} *is in standard form. What is its value?*

The Earth is about 1.5×10^{11} metres from the Sun.

Light travels at a speed of 3.0×10^8 metres per second.

How long does it take light to travel from the Sun to the Earth?

Kylie works it out like this:

$$\frac{\text{Time in}}{\text{seconds}} = \frac{\text{distance}}{\text{speed}} = \frac{1\cdot5 \times 10^{11}}{3 \times 10^8} = \frac{1\cdot5 \times 10^3}{3} = 500$$

Check this calculation on your calculator.

What is 500 seconds in minutes and seconds?

1 Work out these calculations, and give your answers in standard form.

a) $(4 \times 10^3) + (8 \times 10^4)$ b) $(7 \times 10^6) - (2 \times 10^5)$

c) $(3 \times 10^5) \times (5 \times 10^6)$ d) $(8 \times 10^{11}) \div (5 \times 10^4)$

e) $(2.5 \times 10^{-4}) \times (6 \times 10^{12})$ f) $(7.4 \times 10^{-2}) - (3.8 \times 10^{-3})$

g) $(4.5 \times 10^{-7}) \times (3.2 \times 10^{-11})$ h) $(4 \times 10^7)^2$

2 Complete this table by multiplying volume by density to get mass.

Planet	Volume (m^3)	Density (kg/m^3)	Mass (kg)
Mercury	1.45×10^{19}	5.42×10^3	
Venus	9.29×10^{20}	5.25×10^3	
Mars	5.21×10^{19}	3.94×10^3	
Jupiter	1.56×10^{24}	1.31×10^3	

3 The kinetic energy, E, of an electron is $\frac{1}{2} mv^2$.

When $m = 9 \times 10^{-31}$ kg and $v = 2 \times 10^7$ metres per second, what is E?

4 This table shows the population and area of different continents.

Continent	Population	Area (km^2)
Europe (incl Russia)	4.95×10^8	4.94×10^6
Africa	7.43×10^8	3.03×10^7
Oceania	8.51×10^6	2.5×10^7

a) Population density = population ÷ area.

   Which of these continents has the highest population density?

b) What is the population of Oceania to the nearest million?

c) What is the area of Africa to the nearest million km^2?

5 The radius, r, of the moon is 1.7×10^6 metres.

Its volume, V, is $\frac{4}{3}\pi r^3$.

a) What is the volume of the moon?

b) The mass of the moon is 7.4×10^{22} kg.

   What is the density of the moon in kg/m^3?

Find out the radius of each planet in metres.
Set up a spreadsheet to work out the volume of each planet in m^3.

Finishing off

Now that you have finished this chapter you should be able to

★ work out powers and roots of numbers

★ work out the value of numbers in standard form

★ write numbers in standard form

★ do calculations with numbers in standard form.

Use the questions in the next exercise to check that you understand everything.

Mixed exercise

1 Work out

a) 8^2 b) 10^3 c) 6^{-1} d) 4^0

e) 2^7 f) $\sqrt{36}$ g) 12^2 h) $\sqrt[3]{8}$

i) 3^{-2} j) 6^4 k) 5^0 l) 4^{-3}

m) $\sqrt{225}$ n) 7^{-2} o) $\sqrt[3]{64}$ p) 2^{10}

2 Work these out, giving your answer in index form.

For example $3^2 \times 3^5 = 3^7$

a) $2^5 \times 2^3$ b) $7^4 \div 7$ c) $(5^3)^2$ d) $4^2 \times 4^6$

e) $6^5 \div 6^2$ f) $(4^2)^2$ g) $3^5 \times 3 \times 3^{-2}$ h) $\sqrt{3^2}$

3 The numbers in this question are in standard form. Write them out in full.

a) The radius of the Earth is 6.4×10^6 metres

b) A capillary tube has radius 2×10^{-4} metres

c) The wavelength of mercury green light is 5.4×10^{-7} metres

d) The density of mercury is 1.36×10^4 kg/m^3

4 Write these numbers in standard form.

a) A train has a mass of **200 000** kg.

b) The thickness of a piece of cardboard is **0.0015** metres.

c) Thorium-230 has a half life of **83 000** years.

d) The linear expansivity of aluminium is **0.000 026** per degree Kelvin.

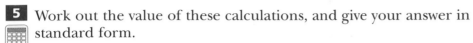

Indices and standard form

5 Work out the value of these calculations, and give your answer in standard form.

a) $(5 \times 10^4) + (8 \times 10^5)$

b) $(3.1 \times 10^{-2}) - (7 \times 10^{-3})$

c) $(4 \times 10^8) \times (9.7 \times 10^{13})$

d) $(3.6 \times 10^{12}) \div (9 \times 10^4)$

e) $(3.2 \times 10^{14}) \times (7.5 \times 10^{-9})$

f) $(4.9 \times 10^{11}) \div (2.8 \times 10^{-5})$

g) $(4.5 \times 10^7)^2$

h) $\sqrt{1.6 \times 10^{13}}$

6 The diameter of the Earth is 1.28×10^7 metres.

Work out the distance around the equator in metres.

7 a) Calculate the number of seconds in a year.

b) Light travels at 3×10^8 metres per second.

How many metres does light travel in a year?

> A light year is the distance travelled by light in a year

c) How many kilometres is this?

d) Sirius A is a star 4.2 light years away from Earth. How many kilometres is this?

Investigation

When you listen to a radio station you must tune in to the appropriate frequency. The frequency is often written in kilohertz (kHz).
It is sometimes written in Hertz (Hz) and then the wavelength, λ, is given by $\lambda = v/f$ where f is the frequency.

> v stands for the speed of the radio waves

Copy and complete this table. (Note. f is required in kHz in the table but must be in Hz to use in the formula, and $v = 3 \times 10^8 \text{ ms}^{-1}$.)

Station	f(kHz)	f(Hz)	λ(m)
Radio 4	198		
Radio 4			417
Talk Radio	1089		
Radio 5 Live			433
Radio 5 Live	909		
Virgin			247
World Service	648		

Find out what these prefixes mean:
a) mega-   b) micro-   c) giga-   c) nano-

Try to find examples of when they are used in real life.

Nine

Manipulating expressions

Before you start this chapter you should be able to

★ expand brackets

★ find the common factors of a set of numbers.

Like terms

Look at these expressions

a) $8a + b$ b) $8x + x^2$ c) $8x^2 + 6x^2$ d) $8ab + 5ba$

Can they be simplified?

a) The terms in $8a + b$ contain different unknowns, a and b, so they are **unlike terms**. It cannot be simplified.

b) The two terms in $8x + x^2$ contain the same unknown, x, but to different powers. Terms in x and x^2 are also unlike terms, and so the expression cannot be simplified.

c) The terms $8x^2$ and $6x^2$ are **like** terms. $8x^2 + 6x^2 = 14x^2$.

d) The terms $8ab$ and $5ba$ are like, because ab and ba are the same ($a \times b = b \times a$). $8ab + 5ba = 13ab$ (or $13ba$).

You can add and subtract like terms to simplify an expression. But you cannot simplify an expression that has no like terms.

Example

Simplify $8a + 5a^2 + 5 + 8a^2 - a + 8 - 4a \times a$

Solution

Collect like terms $5 + 8 + 8a - a + 5a^2 + 8a^2 - 4a^2$ (*This is $4a \times a$*)

Tidy up $13 \qquad + 7a \qquad + 9a^2$

Example

Simplify $5x(1 + x) - 2x + x^2$ (*All the terms here are unlike*)

Solution

$5x(1 + x) - 2x + x^2$ (*Expand the brackets*)

$= 5x + 5x^2 - 2x + x^2$

$= 5x - 2x + 5x^2 + x^2$ (*Collect like terms*)

$= 3x + 6x^2$ (*Tidy up*)

1 State whether these pairs of expressions are identical (the same whatever the value of the letters).

a) zx and xz b) $2 \times t \times t$ and $2t^2$ c) 2 and $2t^2$

d) $2x$ and x^2 e) $3(c+5)$ and $3c+5$ f) $7(1+k)$ and $7+7k$

2 Separate each of these into two separate lists of like terms, then add together the like terms.

a) $2x^2, 4x, 3x^2, 7x$

b) $y^2, 3y, 2y^2, y, -y^2$

c) $3u^2, 4u, -2u, u, 6u^2, -2u$

d) $3p, -3p^2, 3, 6p, 5p^2, 2, 6p, -6$

3 Copy each of these and simplify it by collecting together the like terms. Remember to work down your page.

a) $3x + 2y + 5x + y$ b) $6a + b + 4a + 9b$ c) $2p + 3q + p + q$

d) $5s + 7t + 5s + 2t$ e) $3l + 8m + 5m + 2l$ f) $3g + 2h - 3g + 3h$

g) $x + 5 + 3x - 2$ h) $5x - 2y - 3 - 3x + 6$

i) $4a - 3b - 3c + 2a + 3b - 3c$ j) $3p - 2q + 5p + 2q + 6 + 5$

4 Copy each of these and simplify it by collecting together the like terms.

a) $x^2 + 3x - x + 1$ b) $x^2 - 4x + 2x - 3$ c) $y^2 - 2y - y + 2$

d) $2y^2 - 3y + 7 + y$ e) $5a^2 + 2a + 3a^2 - 3a$ f) $7 - 2x - 3x + x^2$

g) $21 + 6d - 8d - 21$ h) $10x^2 + 6 - 3x - 4 + 2x$ i) $9x - x^2 + 3x - 4x^2$

j) $t^2 + 3t - 3t + 9$

5 Expand the brackets and collect the like terms.

a) $m(3 + m) + m^2$ b) $k + 2k(1 + k)$ c) $4x(5 + x) - 2x^2$

d) $y^2 + y(4 - y)$ e) $x(x + 2) - 4(x + 2)$ f) $a(a + 2) + 2(a + 2)$

g) $h(1 + h) + 5(1 - h)$ h) $h(h - 3) - 6(h - 3)$ i) $x^2(1 + x) - 3x^3$

Investigation

Show that $1 + 2 + 2^2 + 2^3 + 2^4 + 2^5 + 2^6 = 2^7 - 1$

How can you generalise this result?

Factorising

What are the common factors of 12 and 16?

What are the common factors of $12a$ and $16a^2$?

The expression $3x + 12$ has two terms. 3 is a common factor.

> Divide each term by the common factor, and put the factor outside the bracket.

You can write the expression as $3(x + 4)$.

Writing $3x + 12$ as $3(x + 4)$ is called **factorising** the expression. Factorising is just the reverse of expanding the brackets.

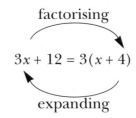

factorising

$$3x + 12 = 3(x + 4)$$

expanding

Example

Factorise   a) $2x + 4y - 6$ b) $15x^2 - 3x$

Solution

a)
$$2x + 4y - 6$$

> The number 2 is a common factor. Write it outside a bracket.

$$= 2(\qquad)$$

> Decide what goes inside. Remember to divide each term by 2.

$$= 2(x + 2y - 3)$$

Check: Expand the bracket: $2 \times x + 2 \times 2y - 2 \times 3 = 2x + 4y - 6$ ✔

b)
$$15x^2 - 3x$$

> The number 3 is a factor.

$$= 3(5x^2 - x)$$

> The unknown, x, is also a factor

> You cannot factorise this any further

$$= 3x(5x - 1)$$

Check: Expand the bracket: $3x \times 5x - 3x \times 1 = 15x^2 - 3x$ ✔

Example

Simplify $2(2x + 5y) + 3(x + 6y)$, giving your answer in factorised form.

Solution

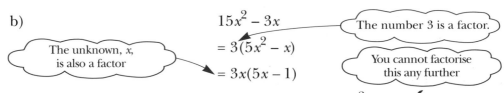

$$2(2x + 5y) + 3(x + 6y)$$

Expand brackets $4x + 10y + \quad 3x + 18y$

Collect like terms $4x + 3x \quad + 10y + 18y$

(Tidy up) $7x \quad + 28y$

Factorise $7(x + 4y)$

1 Write down the common factors of each set of terms.

a) $12, 4x$ b) $3x, 12y, 9$ c) $7a^2, 5a$ d) $25b^2, 15b$

2 Decide on the common factor in each of these sets of terms.

Write each term as the common factor $\times$ something else.

a) $12, 3c$ b) $16, 8y$ c) $7n^2, n$

In these there is more than one common factor.

d) $5x^2, 10x$ e) $14y, 7y^2$ f) $4x^2, 6x$

3 Factorise these expressions. Remember to copy out each one and work down your page.

Check your answers by expanding the brackets.

a) $4t + 8$ b) $6 - 3m$ c) $2 + 18b$

d) $5x + 10$ e) $9z - 33$ f) $5x - 5$

g) $2a + 6b + 4c$ h) $3x - 3y + 9z$ i) $4a - 22b + 6c$

j) $8p + 6q - 4r$ k) $14l - 7m - 49n$ l) $16a + 24b - 32c$

4 Factorise these expressions and check your answers.

a) $2x + x^2$ b) $3y - 2y^2$ c) $5x^2 - 4x$

d) $10y^2 + 7y$ e) $3x^2 + 12x + 6$ f) $21 + 7x - 14x^2$

g) $8g^2 - 16g - 4$ h) $15 + 5x + 20x^2$ i) $6y^2 - 12yx$

j) $3xy^2 - 11y^2$ k) $4st + 8t$ l) $3ab - 6ac + 9ad$

5 For each of the following expressions

(i) expand the brackets
(ii) simplify it by collecting like terms
(iii) factorise the answer to (ii) if possible.

a) $3(x + 2y) + 5(x + 6y)$ b) $4(2x + 3) + 3(x + 7)$

c) $4(3p + 2q) + 3(p + 4q)$ d) $5(x + y) + 3(x - 2y) + 2(x + 3y)$

e) $6(3a - b + 2c) + 2(a + 3b + 2c)$ f) $2(l + m + n) + 3(l - m + n) + m$

g) $3(x + 2y) - 2(x + 4y) + 5(x + 4y)$ h) $12(3p + 2q) - 4(2p + q) - 3(7p + 2q)$

i) $5(x - 2y - 3z) - 3(x - 2y - 5z)$ j) $-2(r - s) - 4(2r - 3s) + 12(r - s)$

k) $x(x - 3) + 3(x + 3)$ l) $x(x - 4) - 4(x - 4) - 16$

Expanding two brackets

You have already expanded expressions like $2(x+3)$ and $x(x+3)$. You know that you have to multiply each term inside the bracket by the term outside it.

How would you do $(x+2)(x+3)$?

Start like this

$$x(x+3) + 2(x+3)$$
$$x^2 + 3x + 2x + 6$$

Now collect like terms $\qquad x^2 + 5x + 6$

Check your answer by putting in $x = 10$ and working out 12×13

You need to multiply each number in the first bracket by each number in the second.

One order for doing this is **F**irst **O**utsides **I**nsides **L**asts (remember it as **FOIL**).

If you join the numbers as you multiply, the lines look like a smiley face.

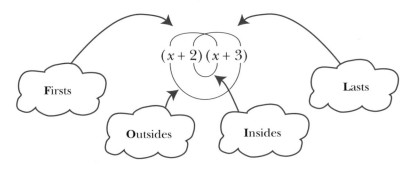

$$x^2 + 3x + 2x + 6$$
$$x^2 + 5x + 6.$$

Use this method to work out 102×104 without a calculator.

Example

Expand $(2x-5)(x-3)$.

Solution

F   O   I   L

$$2x \times x + 2x \times (-3) + (-5) \times x + (-5) \times (-3)$$
$$2x^2 - 6x - 5x + 15$$

$$2x^2 - 11x + 15$$

1 Write these as briefly as possible.

a) $2a \times 3$ b) $2c \times 3c$ c) $4y \times 5y$

d) $-3 \times 2x$ e) $3 \times (-4x)$ f) $-3x \times (-5)$

2 Expand and then simplify each of these.

a) $(x+1)(x+3)$ b) $(y+2)(y+5)$ c) $(4+x)(3+x)$

d) $(5+y)(6+y)$ e) $(x-1)(x+2)$ f) $(y+3)(y-2)$

g) $(x-6)(x+2)$ h) $(y+1)(y-5)$ i) $(x-7)(x-2)$

j) $(y-3)(y-4)$ k) $(x-3)(x-5)$ l) $(y-6)(y-5)$

3 a) Calculate 21^2 by expanding $(20+1)(20+1)$.

b) Calculate 31^2 by the same method.

c) Expand $(x+1)^2 = (x+1)(x+1)$.

d) Use your answers to part c) to find 41^2 without a calculator.

4 Expand each of these and then simplify your answer.

a) $(a+3)(a+3)$ b) $(x+5)^2$ c) $(a-3)(a-3)$

d) $(x-5)^2$ e) $(2y+1)^2$ f) $(3x+2)^2$

5 Expand and then simplify these.

a) $(2x+5)(3x+2)$ b) $(2x-5)(3x-2)$

c) $(2x+5)(3x-2)$ d) $(2x-5)(3x+2)$

6 Expand each of these into 4 terms.

a) $(x+1)(y+1)$ b) $(a+3)(d+2)$ c) $(x-1)(y-1)$

d) $(c+4)(k-10)$ e) $(a-3)(x+4)$ f) $(x+10)(y-1)$

7 The rectangle in the diagram has sides of length $(x+1)$ and $(x+2)$.

a) Write down an expression for its area.

b) Write down the area of each smaller part: A, B, C and D.

c) Expand $(x+1)(x+2)$.

d) Which rectangles correspond to the middle term of c)?

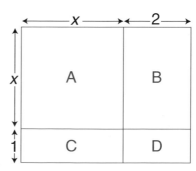

Squares

Squaring brackets

You can write $(a + b)(a + b)$ as $(a + b)^2$.

Look at this square.

Its sides have length $(a + b)$,

so its area is $(a + b)^2$.

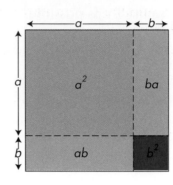

It is made up of 4 rectangles.
When you add their areas you get

$$a^2 + ab + ba + b^2 = a^2 + 2ab + b^2$$

It is important to remember that $(a + b)^2$ is *not* just $a^2 + b^2$.
There is a middle term $+2ab$.

Forgetting the $+2ab$ is like forgetting to include the two blue rectangles!

Expand $(a - b)(a - b)$. Be careful with the signs.

Check your answer by substituting $a = 10$ and $b = 1$.

The difference of two squares

When you multiply $(a + b) \times (a - b)$

you get $a^2 - b^2$.

This is a useful result. It is called
the **difference of two squares**.

It is often written
$$a^2 - b^2 = (a + b)(a - b)$$

so when $a = 10$ and b = 1

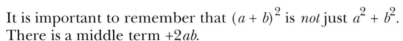

$$a^2 - ab + ba - b^2$$
$$= a^2 - b^2$$

$$\left. \begin{array}{l} 10^2 - 1^2 = 100 - 1 \\ \text{and } (10 + 1)(10 - 1) = 11 \times 9 \end{array} \right\} \text{ These are equal } ✔$$

Use some other values of a and b to check that $a^2 - b^2 = (a + b)(a - b)$.

Work out $143^2 - 142^2$ without using a calculator.

On this page you have met three important results.

$$(a + b)^2 = a^2 + 2ab + b^2$$
$$(a - b)^2 = a^2 - 2ab + b^2$$
$$(a + b)(a - b) = a^2 - b^2$$

> These are all worth remembering.
> They are true when you replace *a* and *b* with any letters or numbers.

1 a) Choose a number for x and draw a square with sides x units on squared paper.

    b) Work out $2x$ and draw another square with sides $2x$.

    c) How many of your first square will fit into your second?

    d) What is another way to write $(2x)^2$?

2 Simplify each of these.

    a) $3x \times 3x$ b) $5y \times 5y$ c) $(3x)^2$

    d) $(5y)^2$ e) $(4a)^2$ f) $(10n)^2$

3 Expand these brackets.

    a) $(x+4)(x+4)$ b) $(y+3)^2$ c) $(c-3)^2$

    d) $(n-5)^2$ e) $(2x+5)(2x+5)$ f) $(3+2t)^2$

    g) $(2y-3)^2$ h) $(5d-1)^2$ i) $(x-4)(x+4)$

    j) $(y+3)(y-3)$ k) $(2x-5)(2x+5)$ l) $(3+2t)(3-2t)$

4 Use the results on the opposite page to write down the answers to these.

    a) $(x+y)^2$ b) $(x-y)^2$ c) $(x+7)^2$

    d) $(x-7)^2$ e) $(2x+3)^2$ f) $(4n-3)^2$

    g) $(5+z)^2$ h) $(3-x)^2$ i) $(2x+3y)^2$

    j) $(2x-3y)^2$ k) $(x+y)(x-y)$ l) $(x+7)(x-7)$

    m) $(2x+1)(2x-1)$ n) $(4n-9)(4n+9)$ o) $(5+z)(5-z)$

    p) $(3p-q)(3p+q)$ q) $(2x+3y)(2x-3y)$ r) $(10a-2b)(10a+2b)$

5 a) Write 19×21 using the numbers 20 and 1.

    b) Explain how you could calculate 19×21 using two squares.

    c) Work out 29×31 in a similar way.

Draw two squares on squared paper as shown (you choose a and b). Then cut out 2 rectangles each with sides a and b.

Cover your squares with your two rectangles so that you are left with a small square with sides $(a-b)$.

Draw a diagram to show what you have done; mark on it the separate areas. What does this illustrate?

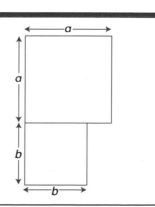

Finishing off

Now that you have finished this chapter you should be able to

★ factorise expressions by taking out a common factor

★ square a bracket

★ expand two brackets and simplify the result.

Use the questions in the next exercise to check that you understand everything.

Mixed exercise

1 Factorise each of these.

a) $20s + 15$ b) $26z - 13y$ c) $18d + 6c - 3b$

d) $2x + x^2$ e) $t^2 - 12t$ f) $5x^2 - 15x$

2 In each of these, expand the brackets and collect like terms.
If possible, factorise the answer.

a) $2(3x + y) + 4(x + 2y)$ b) $5(3p + 7) - 2(4p + 7)$ c) $3(2a - 5b) - 5(a - 3b)$

d) $k + 2k(1 - k)$ e) $4x(3 + 2x) - 7x^2$ f) $a(a + 6) - 5(a + 12)$

3 Expand each of these and simplify the result.

a) $(x + 12)(x + 11)$ b) $(x + 7)(x - 5)$ c) $(x - 9)(x + 6)$

d) $(x - 11)(x + 3)$ e) $(x - 20)(x - 1)$ f) $(x - 13)(x - 3)$

g) $(2x + 5)(x + 1)$ h) $(3x + 4)(5x - 6)$ i) $(a + 3)(4a - 3)$

4 Write each of these without brackets.

a) $(7b)^2$ b) $(3t)^2$ c) $(3x)^3$

d) $(2x^2)^2$ e) $(2x^2)^3$

5 Expand each of these.

a) $(x + 1)^2$ b) $(y + 4)^2$ c) $(t - 3)^2$

d) $(b - 5)^2$ e) $(2x + 1)^2$ f) $(3x - 2)^2$

g) $(6y - 1)^2$ h) $(x^2 + 1)^2$ i) $(1 + x)^2$

6 Expand each of these.

   a) $(x + y)^2$ b) $(x + 2y)^2$ c) $(x + y)(x + 2y)$

   d) $(x - y)(x + 2y)$ e) $(2a + 2b)^2$ f) $(2(a + b))^2$

7 Expand each of these.

   a) $(x - 1)(x + 1)$ b) $(a - 5)(a + 5)$

   c) $(n + 7)(n - 7)$ d) $(2x + 1)(2x - 1)$

   e) $(3t - 4)(3t + 4)$ f) $(x + 2y)(x - 2y)$

8 Pythagoras' rule states that in the right-angled triangle,

$$a^2 + b^2 = c^2$$

This can also be written as $a^2 = c^2 - b^2$.

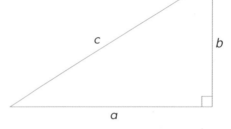

   a) Show that $(c - b)(c + b) = c^2 - b^2$

   b) When $c = 13$ and $b = 12$, show that $a^2 = 25$. What is a in this case?

   c) Find a when $c = 25$ and $b = 24$.

9 Using the fact that $(a - b)(a + b) = a^2 - b^2$, work these out.

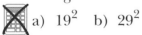

   a) $17^2 - 7^2$ b) $7.6^2 - 2.4^2$

10 Using the fact that $(a + b)^2 = a^2 + 2ab + b^2$, work these out.

   a) 31^2 b) 41^2

11 Using the fact that $(a - b)^2 = a^2 - 2ab + b^2$, work these out.

   a) 19^2 b) 29^2

12 a) Expand $(x + 1)(y + 1)$.

   b) Substitute $x = 20$ and $y = 30$ into your answer and check it is the same as 21×31.

   c) Use your answer to a) to calculate 31×61.

13 a) Expand $(x + 1)(x - 1)$.

   b) Use your answer to part a) to calculate 21×19 and 51×49.

   c) Use a similar method to calculate 22×18 and 48×52.

Ten

Probability

Before you start this chapter you should

★ know that probability can be represented on a scale from 0 to 1

★ be able to estimate probabilities from past data

★ be able to calculate the probability of a particular outcome from theory.

Use the following questions to check you still remember these topics.

Reminder

- P(A) means the probability of event A occurring.

- P(not A) = 1 − P(A)

1 Draw a probability scale. Mark on your scale the following points, and for each one say whether its position on the scale is exact or approximate. The probability that

A a tossed coin will land showing tails

B you will break the world land speed record on your bicycle

C you will take at least one breath in the next 5 minutes

D it will rain tomorrow

E you will dig up a valuable old coin in your garden

F there is a point marked **F** on your scale.

2 Fran has planted 3 hyacinth bulbs in separate pots, to give to relations at Christmas. One of the bulbs is pink, one is blue and one is white. She cannot remember which is which, and the flowers are not yet showing.

Fran picks two at random to give to her grandmothers.

a) Estimate the probability that one is blue and the other is white.

b) Estimate the probability that one is white.

Revision Exercise

3 A driving school prepares learners for the driving test and only allows them to take the test when they are competent, and should pass. However, some people do still fail and the school believes that this happens at random.

Of the 125 people who started learning with the school in January, 100 passed first time, 20 passed second time and 4 passed third time.

Estimate the probability that a learner from this driving school will

a) pass at the first attempt

b) pass at the second attempt

c) pass at the third attempt

d) fail three driving tests.

4 Craig is an amateur astronomer.

He keeps this 'shooting star' diary one April, recording a tick each night that he sees one, a cloud each night the sky is obscured by cloud, and a cross each clear night that he does not see a shooting star.

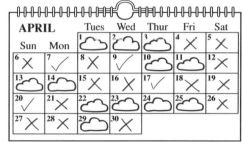

a) Use the diary data to predict the probability that Craig will see a shooting star on any night next April.

b) Estimate the probability that the sky is hidden by cloud on any night.

c) On how many of the cloudy nights do you think there would have been shooting stars? Explain your reasoning.

d) Do you think that Craig has collected enough data to make confident estimates of these probabilities?

5 You are playing Monopoly. You throw a red die and a blue die. Your score is the sum of the two numbers.

a) Copy and complete this table showing the possible outcomes.

b) From your table work out the probability of scoring

(i) 7, which means you go to jail

(ii) 2 or 12, which means you can buy a station

(iii) 11, which means you pay a lot of rent

(iv) 10, which means you take a card from Community Chest

(v) a double, which means you get a second throw.

Red die score

Blue die score	1	2	3	4	5	6
1	2		4			
2						
3						
4						
5						
6		8				

Two outcomes: 'either, or'

Avonford Car Auctions holds a monthly Company Draw. One employee is picked (at random) by the company computer to win £200.

This week several people are off work because of a flu epidemic, and some people are away on courses.

What is the probability that the employee who wins the draw is absent, either with flu or on a course?

Absences 15th June

flu   7
courses   12
working   31
_____
TOTAL   50

You can see that there are 50 employees in total, so there are 50 possible winners. Of those 50:

7 have flu: $P(\text{flu}) = \dfrac{7}{50}$

12 are away on a course: $P(\text{course}) = \dfrac{12}{50}$

> Nobody with flu is on the course. They are all in bed.

Of the 50 employees, a total of 19 are away either with flu or on a course, so you can write

$$P(\text{flu or course}) = \frac{19}{50}$$

Notice that in this case,

$$P(\text{flu or course}) = P(\text{flu}) + P(\text{course})$$

> To find the probability that the winner either has flu or is on a course you can add the probability that the winner has flu and the probability that the winner is on a course

Of the 50 employees, 31 are in the sports club and 10 are in the fell-walking club. What is the probability that the winner is in one of these clubs?

You may have realised that to answer the question you need more information. Some of the fell-walkers may also be in the sports club: the outcomes are not **mutually exclusive**

In fact, Ted, Liz and Nina are in both clubs. You want to add the probabilities without counting these people twice, so you can write

$$P(\text{sports or fell}) = P(\text{sports}) + P(\text{fell but not sports}) = \frac{31}{50} + \frac{7}{50} = \frac{38}{50}$$

> There are 10 people in the fell-walking club but 3 have already been counted in the sports club.
> $10 - 3 = 7$

You can add the probabilities in 'either, or' situations, provided you make sure that the outcomes do not overlap.

How many people, altogether, are involved in the sports club or the fell-walking club?

1 When you select a card at random from an ordinary pack, what is the probability that it is either

a) a king or a queen?   b) a king or a heart?

2 Dick plants mixed crocuses: 5 purple, 7 yellow and 8 white.

Work out the probability that the first one to flower in the Spring will be

a) purple   b) yellow or white   c) purple or white

d) neither purple nor white.

3 Paul is a keen bird-watcher. One June he keeps a close watch on 65 nests of house-martins. He records the number of hatchlings in each one that survive and fly the nest. This is his table of the results.

Number of hatchlings flying the nest	0	1	2	3	4	5	6
Frequency (number of nests)	1	5	12	18	24	3	2

Using Paul's data, estimate the probability that a nest of house-martins will produce

a) 5 hatchlings that fly the nest

b) at least 4 hatchlings that fly the nest

c) fewer than 3 hatchlings that fly the nest.

4 Make a table to show all the possible scores when two fair dice (one red, one blue) are thrown.

Find the probability that

a) the scores are the same (it is a double)

b) the score on the red die is greater than the score on the blue one

c) both dice show odd numbers

d) the total score is more than 7.

You are going to check whether real dice behave as your answers to question 4b) suggest. Find two dice of different colours. Draw a table like the one you drew for question 4 to record your results.

The relative frequency each time is the number of times red has scored more than blue, divided by the total number of throws so far.

You would expect the relative frequency to get closer and closer to your calculated probability. Is this noticeable after 10 throws? Extend the table, and see if it is closer after 20 throws, or 50 throws.

Two outcomes: 'first, then'

When you select a playing card at random from an ordinary pack, the probability of selecting an ace is $\frac{4}{52}$. (There are 4 aces in the pack, and 52 cards altogether.) When you select one card, then replace it, then select another, the probability of an ace is $\frac{4}{52}$ each time.

What is the probability that both cards are aces?

In this situation, when you want to work out the probability of first one outcome, then another happening, you multiply the probabilities.

$$\frac{4}{52} \times \frac{4}{52} = \frac{1}{13} \times \frac{1}{13} = \frac{1}{169}$$

The probability that both cards are aces is $\frac{1}{169}$

What is the probability that both cards are black?

Sometimes two events happen at the same time, but you can still think of them as first one, then another.

Example

Calum goes into a shop to buy 2 light bulbs. He cannot tell from the packaging, but 6 of the 25 light bulbs on the shelf are faulty.

What is the probability that he picks up 2 faulty bulbs?

Solution

When he chooses his first bulb, the probability of a faulty one is $\frac{6}{25}$.

When he chooses his second bulb, the probability of a faulty one is different. There are 24 bulbs left, of which 5 are faulty.

The probability of a faulty one is $\frac{5}{24}$.

The probability that Calum picks two faulty bulbs is $\frac{6}{25} \times \frac{5}{24} = \frac{1}{20}$.

> These events are not independent; the outcome of the first affects the probability of the second.

What is the probability that Calum picks two good bulbs?

What is the probability that he picks one faulty and one good?

What combination is Calum most likely to pick?

In 'first, then' situations, you multiply the probabilities, but you need to think carefully about those probabilities when the events are not independent.

1 Two coins are tossed. Find the probability that

a) both land showing Heads

b) one lands showing Heads, the other Tails.

2 Angela, Basil and Connie travel to a meeting by train from different directions. Every train has a probability of 0.1 of being late, and you can treat them as independent events.

Find the probability that

a) Connie is late

b) Connie and Basil are both late

c) Connie and Basil are late but Angela's train is on time

d) all three trains are on time.

3 Three coins are tossed. Find the probability that they land showing

a) three Heads

b) two Heads and a Tail (in that order)

c) two Tails and a Head (in that order)

d) two Tails and a Head (in any order)

e) three Tails.

4 Rowena does a survey of pedestrians in Avonford town centre. She asks them how they have travelled there, and the main purpose of their visit. She presents the results in these pie charts.

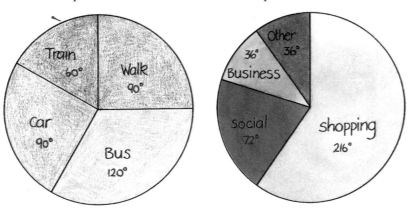

Using Rowena's pie charts, work out the probability that a pedestrian chosen at random

a) has travelled into Avonford on foot

b) is there mainly for a social event.

Assuming that the events are independent, what is the probability that a pedestrian chosen at random

c) arrived on foot for a social event?

d) arrived by train for business?

e) arrived by bus or train for a shopping trip?

Probability trees

The probability that a person (chosen at random) is left-handed is $\frac{1}{10}$. The probability that a person wears glasses is $\frac{1}{4}$.

What is the probability that a person chosen at random is left-handed and wears glasses?

What is the probability that the person is right-handed and wears glasses?

You can work out these probabilities using the ideas from the previous pages. Alternatively you can represent the situation in a **tree diagram**, which shows the probabilities of all possible outcomes.

Any person is taken to be either left-handed or right-handed: two alternatives. You show this as two branches of a 'tree', and write the probability on each branch.

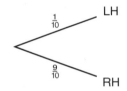

Any person either wears glass or doesn't. Again there are two alternatives. You extend the diagram like this.

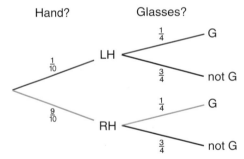

The probability that a person is left-handed and wears glasses is given by multiplying the probabilities along the red branches:

$$\text{P(LH and G)} = \frac{1}{10} \times \frac{1}{4} = \frac{1}{40}$$

The probability that a person is right-handed and wears glasses is given by

$$\text{P(RH and G)} = \frac{9}{10} \times \frac{1}{4} = \frac{9}{40} \text{ (the green branches)}$$

There are four possible outcomes. The probabilities of two of them have been found above. Find the probabilities of the other two outcomes, and add all four probabilities together.

What does this tell you?

Probability trees are particularly helpful when there are more than two outcomes from each event, and when the events are not independent.

1 A student survey finds that 60% of students own a bicycle and 70% own a CD player. Assuming these to be independent, draw a probability tree and find the probability that a randomly chosen student owns

a) a bicycle but no CD player

b) a CD player but no bicycle

c) neither a CD player nor a bicycle

d) both a CD player and a bicycle.

2 Fred claims to be able to tell the colour of a Smartie by taste alone. A test is organised with Fred blindfolded. He has to pick 30 Smarties out of a big bowl containing equal numbers of red, green and brown Smarties. He eats each one and says what colour he thinks it is.

a) How many out of the 30 would you expect Fred to get right if

(i) his claim is false and he is just guessing?

(ii) his claim is true and he really can tell them apart?

b) In fact Fred can tell the green ones but guesses between the red and brown.

Copy and complete this tree diagram for the situation.

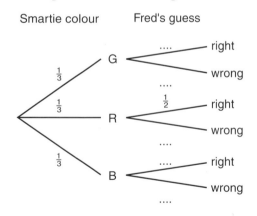

c) What is the probability that Fred gets a Smartie right?

d) In fact Fred gets 21 right. Is that about what you would expect?

Set up and carry out an experiment like the one in question 2. Write a short report on your findings, including tree diagrams to show what the probabilities appear to be.

Finishing off

Now that you have finished this chapter you should be able to

★ work out the probability of a particular outcome in an 'either, or' situation

★ work out the probability of a particular outcome in a 'first, then' situation

★ use a tree diagram to work out the probabilities of different outcomes for two or more events.

Use the following questions to check that you still remember these topics.

Mixed exercise

1 Alice draws a card from a pack of cards. Andrew draws a card from a different pack. Find the probability that both cards

a) are the same suit

b) are hearts

c) are the same number (or picture)

d) are court cards (jack, queen or king)

e) are the same colour

f) are *not* court cards.

2 The probability that a person chosen at random can move his or her ears is 0.2, and the probability that the person can roll his or her tongue is 0.4.

a) Draw a probability tree to represent this situation.

b) What is the probability that a person, chosen at random, can move his or her ears *and* tongue-roll?

3 Chris finds that in about 1 out of every 2 golf games he loses a ball. For Dennis, it is about 1 in every 3 games.

Estimate the probability that when they play each other

a) Chris loses a ball but Dennis doesn't

b) Dennis loses a ball but Chris doesn't

c) one (and only one) ball is lost

d) both lose a ball

e) neither loses a ball.

4 The carnation plants at a garden centre have lost their labels and got mixed up. The manager knows that 40% are red, 20% are white, 30% are pink and 10% are yellow.

Amy buys two of the carnation plants. What is the probability that

a) they are both red?

b) they are both white?

c) they are both the same colour?

d) they are different colours?

e) one is red and one is white?

f) one is red and one is not?

5 The probability that a new baby will be a boy is about 0.51.

a) Draw a tree diagram to show the probabilities for a woman who has two children.

b) What is the probability that she has two boys?

c) What is the probability that she has two girls?

d) What is the most likely combination?

6 On Marie's route to work she drives through a junction with traffic lights. The whole traffic light sequence at this junction takes 2 minutes, and it runs as shown in the diagram.

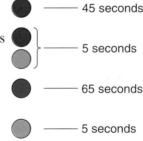

———— 45 seconds

———— 5 seconds

———— 65 seconds

———— 5 seconds

What is the probability that on any journey Marie arrives at the junction when the lights are

a) green?   b) red?   c) red and amber?

One day, Marie drives through the traffic lights 3 times. What is the probability that she arrives

d) at a green light every time?   e) at a red light every time?

Look up Gregor Mendel in an encyclopedia. Read about his experiments involving sweet-peas, and write a short description of them, explaining the importance of his findings.

Mendel's work is the basis for much of modern genetics.

Eleven
Locus

Before you start this chapter you should be able to

★ make accurate drawings, full size or to scale.

Simple loci

The **locus** of a point means all the possible positions for that point.

Ainsley and Sarah are going on a camping holiday. They need to decide where to pitch their tent. Ainsley wants to be no more than 200 m from the shop. The map of the campsite shows the area where he would like to be.

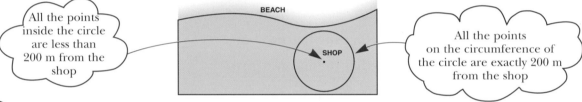

All the points inside the circle are less than 200 m from the shop

All the points on the circumference of the circle are exactly 200 m from the shop

 How could you describe the points outside the circle?

The locus of a point a fixed distance, *d*, from a fixed point O forms a circle, centre O and radius *d*

Sarah wants to be less than 100 m from the beach. The map shows the area where she would like to be.

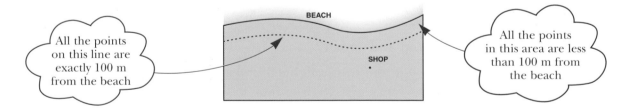

All the points on this line are exactly 100 m from the beach

All the points in this area are less than 100 m from the beach

The locus of a point a fixed distance, *d*, from a line AB forms a line parallel to AB and distance *d* from AB.

 Why is the line in this diagram dotted and not solid?

All the points in the shaded area are both no more than 200 m from the shop and less than 100 m from the beach.

Ainsley and Sarah should camp somewhere in this area.

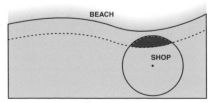

1 For each part, draw this rectangle full size and shade in the required locus. Only shade points inside the rectangle.

a) The locus of all points less than 3 cm from A.

b) The locus of all points more than 2 cm from BC.

c) The locus of all points at least 1 cm from the centre of the rectangle.

d) The locus of all points more than 6 cm from C and more than 5 cm from D.

e) The locus of all points less than 3 cm from AB and at least 2 cm from B.

f) The locus of all points no more than 1 cm from the perimeter of the rectangle.

A   8 cm   B

5 cm

D   C

2 A goat is tied to a point (marked G on the diagram) on the outside of a barn, 3 metres from the corner. The rope is 5 metres long. Make a scale drawing of the diagram and shade in the locus of the points where the goat can go.

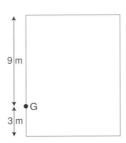

9 m

3 m   •G

3 Molly wants to plant a tree in her garden. She must not plant the tree within 2 metres of the house. Molly's house is 12 m long and 10 m wide. Make a scale drawing of the house and shade in the locus of the points where Molly must *not* plant the tree.

4 Keith is looking for somewhere to live. He wants to be no more than 3 miles away from the station as he catches a train to work every morning. He is also a keen cinema-goer and would like to be no more than 5 miles away from the local cinema. The station and the cinema are 6.5 miles apart.

Make a scale drawing and show the area where Keith would like to live.

5 Simon and his brother Mark are playing in a rubber dinghy in the sea. The coastguard has told them not to go more than 50 m from the shore. There is a rock 40 m from the beach and he has also told them not to go within 5 m of the rock.

Make a scale drawing and shade the area where they are allowed to go. (Assume that the shoreline is straight.)

Investigate the locus of a point on the circumference of a bicycle wheel as the bicycle moves along.

A point equidistant from two fixed points

A new road is being built between two villages A and B. So that the new road makes as little disturbance as possible in the two villages, the road is being built so that it is always the same distance from A as from B.

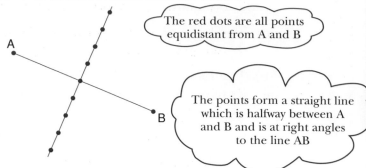

The red dots are all points equidistant from A and B

The points form a straight line which is halfway between A and B and is at right angles to the line AB

The position of the road will be the locus of a point **equidistant** (the same distance) from A and B.

This is called the **perpendicular bisector** of AB.

> **The locus of a point equidistant from two points is the perpendicular bisector of the two points.**

 Where are the points which are nearer to A than to B?

Drawing a perpendicular bisector accurately

These instructions explain how to draw the perpendicular bisector of the line AB.

1. Place your compass point on A. Open the compass to a radius more than half the distance from A to B. Draw an arc each side of AB.

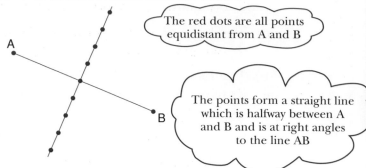

2. Leave the compass at the same radius. Put the compass point on B and make another arc each side of AB, so that they cross the other arcs.

3. Draw a line joining the two intersections. This is the perpendicular bisector.

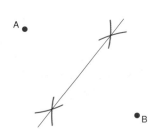

1 a) Mark two points P and Q (not in a horizontal or vertical line). Construct the perpendicular bisector of PQ.

b) Mark 3 points on the perpendicular bisector. Measure the distance of each point from P and from Q to check that it is the same.

2 a) Draw a circle and mark three points, A, B and C on the circumference.

b) Construct the perpendicular bisectors of AB, BC and CA.

c) You should find that they meet at a point.

What is special about the point where they meet?

3 Sophie works in town S and her parents live in town T, 50 miles from town S. She is looking for a place to live somewhere between the two towns. She wants to be nearer to S than to T but would like to be within 30 miles of her parents.

Make a scale drawing and shade the area where Sophie would like to live.

4 The diagram below shows three schools A, B and C in a large town. Mr and Mrs Hammond and their son Michael are moving into the area, and Michael wants to go to school C. The Hammonds need to live somewhere which is nearer to school C than to school A, and nearer to school C than to school B.

Trace the diagram and shade the area where the Hammonds should live.

A •

•
B

C •

Find a map of your area with some of the local schools marked on it. Use perpendicular bisectors to show the areas which are nearer to each school than to any other school.

A point equidistant from two lines

The designer of a new housing estate is putting two houses at the end of a cul-de-sac. She wants the boundary fence between the two houses to be the same distance from the wall of each house. The position of the fence will be the locus of a point equidistant from two lines.

The red dots are all points which are the same distance from each house.

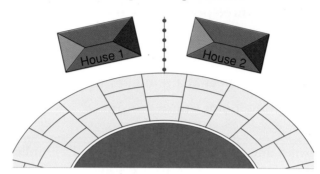

The dots form a straight line which will be the position of the boundary fence.

In this diagram, the lines showing the wall of each house have been extended until they meet, forming an angle. The red line showing the position of the fence has also been extended.

You can see that the fence line cuts the angle formed by the other two lines in half. It is called the **angle bisector**

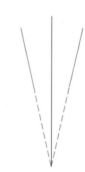

The locus of a point equidistant from two lines is the angle bisector of the two lines.

 Where are the points nearer to house 1 than to house 2?

Drawing an angle bisector accurately

1. Put the compass point on the point of the angle and mark off two points as shown.

2. Put the compass point on each of the points you have marked off and draw two arcs which meet each other.

3. Draw a line through the point where the arcs intersect to the point of the angle. This line is the angle bisector.

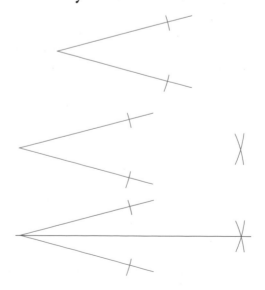

1 a) Draw two lines to make an angle. Construct the angle bisector.

  b) Measure the angle and check that the angle bisector cuts the angle in half.

2 a) Draw a triangle. Construct the angle bisector of each of the three angles of the triangle.

  b) The three angle bisectors should meet at a point. What is special about this point?

3 Trace this triangle four times.

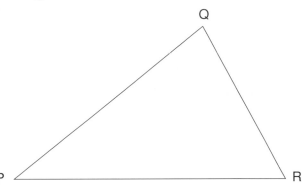

a) On the first diagram, shade the locus of all points nearer to PR than to PQ.

b) On the second diagram, shade the locus of all points nearer to QR than to PQ and within 3 cm of Q.

c) On the third diagram, shade the locus of all points nearer to PR than to QR and nearer to PQ than QR.

d) On the fourth diagram, shade the locus of all points nearer to PQ than to PR and nearer to Q than to P.

4 This diagram shows a field in which there are some rabbits. The field is surrounded by hedges on sides AB, BC and CD. A fox appears at point F and all the rabbits run to the nearest hedge. Trace the field and divide it up, showing the areas which are nearest to each of the three hedges.

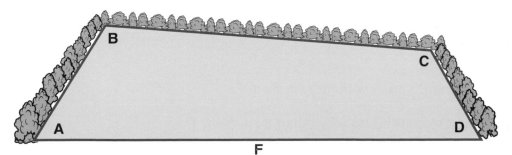

Finishing off

> **Now that you have finished this chapter you should know how to**
>
> ★ construct the perpendicular bisector of a line
>
> ★ construct the bisector of an angle
>
> ★ solve problems involving loci, including intersecting loci
>
> ★ find the locus of a point which is a fixed distance from a point, a fixed distance from a line, equidistant from two points, or equidistant from two lines.

Use the questions in the next exercise to check that you understand everything.

1 Mark a point X. Draw the locus of all points which are less than 4 cm from X.

2 Mark points S and T 5 cm apart (not in a horizontal or vertical line). Draw the locus of all points equidistant from S and T.

3 Draw an angle ABC of size 63°. Draw the locus of all points equidistant from the lines AB and BC.

4 Draw a line XY 3 cm long. Draw the locus of all points exactly 2 cm from XY. (Hint: think carefully what happens to points at each end of the line.)

5 Draw points M and N 8 cm apart (not in a horizontal or vertical line). Draws the locus of all points nearer to M than to N.

For questions 6 to 11, trace the triangle XYZ and shade the locus of the point P. In all cases, P is inside the triangle XYZ.

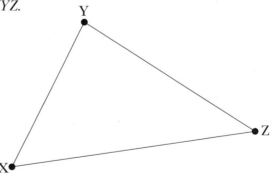

6 P is less than 4 cm from X and less than 5 cm from Z.

7 P is nearer to X than to Z and is no more than 2 cm from Y.

8 P is less than 3 cm from XZ and less than 2 cm from Y.

9 P is no more than 3 cm from X, less than 4 cm from Y and at least 5 cm from Z.

10 P is nearer to XY than to XZ and is more than 1 cm from YZ.

11 P is nearer to Y than to Z and is nearer to YZ than to XY.

12 Jed is at a rock concert. He wants to be equidistant from the two speakers to get the best stereo effect. He also wants to be less than 10 m from the stage.

Make a scale drawing and show the possible places where Jed would like to be.

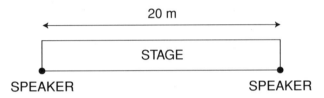

13 This diagram is the plan of a church which is going to be fitted with a burglar alarm inside. Two motion sensors, each with a range of 8 m in all directions, are shown. Make a scale drawing of the church and shade the areas which are not covered by the sensors. (Remember that the sensors do not work round corners!)

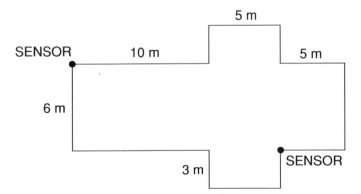

Twelve

Ratio and proportion

Before you start this chapter you should be able to

★ relate a ratio to fractions, decimals and percentages

★ write a ratio in its simplest form

★ share an amount in a given ratio

★ solve problems with ratio.

Use the following questions to check that you still remember these topics.

Revision exercise

1 Gina makes squash by mixing one part orange with 9 parts water.

a) How many millilitres of water are needed for 2 litres of squash?

b) What fraction of the squash is water?

c) What percentage of the squash is orange?

d) Gina has 750 ml of orange and unlimited water. How much squash can she make?

2 Write each ratio in its simplest form.

a) 8:4　　　b) 15:20　　　c) 60:40　　　d) 12:36

e) 14:35　　f) 8:12　　　g) 50:20　　　h) 96:36

i) 6:8:10　j) 40:60:80　k) 6:12:15　l) 48:60:108

3 Write each ratio in a common unit and then put it in its simplest form.

a) 15 minutes:2 hours　　b) 30 mm:2 cm　　c) 750 g:2 kg

d) £5:125p　　　　　　e) 300 ml:1.5 l　　f) 1500 m:10 km

g) 7.5 cm:0.1 m　　　　h) 5 cm:1 km

4 Which is the better buy?

a)

b)

5 a) Share £600 in the ratio 3:2. b) Share £540 in the ratio 2:7.

c) Share £2250 in the ratio 2:3:4. d) Share £3200 in the ratio 4:5:1.

6 Jill and her grandad plan to make 20 lbs of blackberry jam using this recipe.

Blackberry Jam (makes 5lbs)
2lbs blackberries
3lbs sugar
1½ pints water

a) How much of each ingredient do they need?

Jill and her grandad go blackberrying but only collect 5 lbs of blackberries.

b) How many pounds of jam can they make?

c) How much sugar do they need?

7 Simon runs a business. He spent £2000 on advertising last year. This was split between newspaper adverts and leaflets in the ratio 3:2.

a) How much did he spend on newspaper adverts?

b) How much did he spend on leaflets?

Simon checked how effective each method was. Newspaper adverts brought in business worth £42 000, leaflets brought in business worth £14 000.

c) Write the ratio 42 000:14 000 in its simplest form.

d) This year Simon spends 25% more on advertising.

How much does he spend on advertising?

e) He splits what he spends between newspaper adverts and leaflets according to the amount of business they each brought in last year.

How much is spent on leaflets this year?

f) What fraction of Simon's advertising this year is spent on newspaper adverts?

Investigation

Square A has sides of length 3 cm. Work out the perimeter and area.

Square B has sides of length 6 cm. Work out the ratio.

a) perimeter of A : perimeter of B
b) area of A : area of B

What do you notice?

When you double the radius of a circle what happens to the circumference? What happens to the area?

Unitary method

On page 12 Josh bought a computer printer for £170. This was the price after a 15% discount. Josh worked out the price before discount like this:

85% is 170

1% is $\dfrac{170}{85}$

100% is $\dfrac{170}{85} \times 100 = 200$

The usual price is £200.

This method, of first finding 1%, is called the **unitary method**

Why is this a useful technique?

Example

200 g of meat costs £1.44. How much does 340 g cost?

Solution

200 g costs £1.44

1 g costs $\dfrac{£1.44}{200}$

340 g costs $\dfrac{£1.44}{200} \times 340 = £2.448$

> This has to be rounded to give a whole number of pence.

340 g of meat costs £2.45 to the nearest penny.

Example

The exchange rate is £1 = 2.32 Swiss francs. A clock costs 150 Swiss francs. How much is this in pounds and pence?

Solution

You are changing Swiss francs to pounds, so the exchange rate is written as

2.32 Swiss francs is £1

1 Swiss franc is $\dfrac{£1}{2.32}$

150 Swiss francs is $\dfrac{£1}{2.32} \times 150 = £64.655.$

The clock costs £64.66 to the nearest penny.

1 Kristen, Ben, Esther and Lauren are supermarket assistants paid at the same rate.

Kristen works a 35 hour week and earns £190.75.

a) How much does he earn an hour?

b) Ben works 15 hours. How much does he earn?

c) Esther works 37 hours. How much does she earn?

d) What is the least number of hours that Lauren must work to earn over £130?

2 The mass of 5 cm^3 of gold is 96.5 g.

a) What is the mass of 9 cm^3 of gold?

b) What volume of gold has a mass of 1 kg?

3 Loz has this recipe for making 12 cranberry oat bars.

a) How much of each ingredient is needed for 36 cranberry oat bars?

b) Loz has 1 kg of rolled oats, 500 g of golden sugar, 200 g of butter, 250 g of golden syrup and 125 g of cranberries.

What is the greatest number of cranberry oat bars he can make?

12
CRANBERRY OAT BARS
175 g of rolled oats
100 g golden sugar
75 g butter
50 g golden syrup
50 g cranberries

4 Preeti is going to America. Her bank offers an exchange rate of £1 = $1.62.

a) Preeti changes £350 into dollars. How many dollars does she get?

b) In America she spends $45 on a coach tour. How much is this to the nearest pound?

c) Preeti wants to get a small present for her sister. She does not want to spend more than £10 on it. How much is this in dollars?

d) Preeti pays $20 for a concert ticket. How much is this in pounds and pence?

5 Janice types 252 words in 4 minutes 40 seconds. What is her speed in words per minute?

Distance, speed and time

What is the speed limit on motorways?

How fast does an aeroplane fly?

How many metres per second can you run?

Speed is usually measured in miles per hour (m.p.h.), kilometres per hour (km/h) or metres per second (m/s).

Tim drives at 100 km/h on the motorway.

Do you think that he drives at exactly 100 km/h all the time?

Tim drives 90 km on country

roads in $1\frac{1}{2}$ hours.

What is his average speed in km/h?

$$\text{average speed} = \frac{\text{distance covered}}{\text{time taken}}$$

$$= \frac{90}{1\frac{1}{2}} = 60$$

Tim's average speed is 60 km/h.

Kanwal does the same journey in $1\frac{1}{4}$ hours.

What is her average speed?

Tim's average speed on a motorway is 100 km/h.

How long does a motorway journey of 225 km take?

$$\text{time taken} = \frac{\text{distance covered}}{\text{average speed}}$$

$$= \frac{225}{100} = 2.25 \text{ or } 2\frac{1}{4}$$

The time taken is $2\frac{1}{4}$ hours (or 2 hours 15 minutes).

> Be careful here!
> .25 hours is not 25 minutes.
> To change 0.25 hours into minutes you multiply by 60
> $0.25 \times 60 = 15$ so
> 0.25 hours = 15 minutes

How long does it take Tim to travel 60 km?

How far does Tim travel in $1\frac{3}{4}$ hours?

distance covered = average speed $\times$ time taken

$$= 100 \times 1\frac{3}{4} = 175$$

Tim travels 175 km in $1\frac{3}{4}$ hours.

How far does Tim travel in 45 minutes?

1 What distance is covered by

a) Linton cycling at 50 km/h for 2 hours?

b) Jovanka driving at 70 km/h for $1\frac{1}{2}$ hours?

c) Philip flying at 880 km/h for $2\frac{1}{4}$ hours?

d) Liz running at 15 km/h for 1 hour 20 minutes?

2 Hana has four meetings today. This is her schedule.

Work out the average speed

a) between London and Milton Keynes (84 km apart)

b) between Milton Keynes and Leicester (81 km apart)

c) between Leicester and Sheffield (105 km apart)

TUESDAY 6

MEETING
Leave London 10.00
Arrive Milton Keynes 11.30

MEETING
Leave Milton Keynes 12.30
Arrive Leicester 13.45

MEETING
Leave Leicester 14.45
Arrive Sheffield 16.00

MEETING

3 Work out the time it takes to

a) cycle 75 km at 30 km/h

b) fly 2250 km at 600 km/h

c) drive 100 km at 60 km/h

d) run a marathon (42.2 km) at 20 km/h.

4 Darren from Liverpool and Vicky from Hull drive to Manchester to meet for lunch.

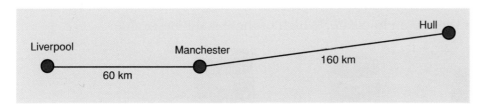

a) Darren leaves home at 1140 and his average speed is 60 km/h. What time does Darren arrive in Manchester?

b) Vicky leaves at 1045 and expects to take 2 hours. What will her average speed be?

c) Vicky's journey takes 30 minutes longer than planned. What is her average speed?

d) How long did Darren have to wait on his own?

Finishing off

Now that you have finished this chapter you should be able to

★ solve problems with ratio

★ use the unitary method

★ solve problems with distance, speed and time.

Use the questions in the next exercise to check that you understand everything.

1 Write each ratio in its simplest form.

a) 9:12

b) 25:40

c) 56:35

d) 16:32:8

e) 40 minutes: $1\frac{1}{2}$ hours

f) 450 g:2 kg

g) 5 cm:1 km

h) 1.5 litres:150 ml

2 £20 000 is shared in the following way. Andrew gets one quarter of it. Harriet gets one fifth of the remainder. Justin and Mel share the rest in the ratio 3:2.

a) How much does each person get?

b) What is the ratio of Andrew's share to Harriet's share in its simplest form?

c) What percentage of the £20 000 does Justin get?

d) What fraction of the money does Mel receive? Write your answer in its simplest form.

3 Kathryn wants some hot chocolate. Which of these is the best value?

 £2·25 200g

 350g £3·59

 450g £4·69

4 George makes concrete by mixing sand, gravel and cement in the ratio 2:4:1.

a) How much of each does George need to make 10.5 m³ of concrete?

b) He has only 2.5 m³ of sand. What is the greatest amount of concrete that he can make?

5 Peter goes to France. The exchange rate is £1 = 9.42 francs.

a) How many francs does Peter get for £240?

b) He pays 2% commission on the £240. How much commission does he pay?

c) He visits a cafe and sees this menu.

Work out the cost of each item in sterling giving your answer to the nearest ten pence.

Paris   Paris

MENU

Boeuf Bourguignon 60F

Poulet-frites 50F

Escalope de veau. 75F

'' 'Vin rouge 45F

Eau minérale 20F

Limonade 15F

6 8.4 g of iron combines with 3.6 g of oxygen to form 12 g of iron oxide.

a) How much oxygen combines with 14 g of iron?

b) How much iron combines with 13.2 g of oxygen?

c) How much of each element is required to produce 50 g of iron oxide?

7 a) Lucy cycles for 45 minutes at an average speed of 30 km/h. How far does she travel?

b) Anant is a airline pilot. He has 900 km to cover in $1\frac{1}{4}$ hours. What average speed does he need to attain?

c) Tracey has 50 km to drive. She thinks her average speed will be 65 km/h. How long, to the nearest 5 minutes, will it take her?

8 Asif plots the distance his coach has travelled against time.
This journey is broken into 3 stages by 2 breaks. This is his graph.

a) What is the average speed for the first stage of the journey?

b) How long was the first break?

c) What is the average speed for the second stage of the journey?

The total distance covered is 315 km.

d) What is the total time taken including breaks?

e) What is the average speed for the whole journey?

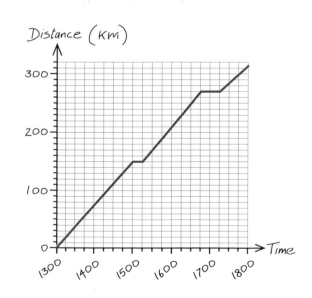

Thirteen

Quadratics

Before you start this chapter you should

★ be familiar with the work in Chapter 9.

Factorising quadratic expressions

In this chapter you learn how to solve quadratic equations. The first step in this is to **factorise** a quadratic expression. This is the opposite of multiplying two brackets together (or expanding them).

The lines are the same, but written in opposite orders.

EXPANDING $(x+2)(x+3)$		FACTORISING x^2+5x+6	
(I usually don't write this line)	$x(x+3)+2(x+3)$	Split the 5x $x^2+3x+2x+6$	3+2=5 3×2=6
I use FOIL	$x^2+3x+2x+6$ F O I L	Factorise in pairs $x(x+3)+2(x+3)$	
Tidy up	$x^2 + 5x + 6$	Finish off $(x+2)(x+3)$	x+3 is in both brackets

Alternatively you can start by writing

$$x^2 + 5x + 6 = (x \quad)(x \quad)$$

Now you need to work out the number term in each bracket

Look for two numbers that multiply to give 6.

They could be 1×6 or 2×3.

Your two numbers must also add up to 5.

They are 2 and 3.

$$x^2 + 5x + 6 = (x + 2)(x + 3)$$

You must check by multiplying out the brackets.

CHECK
$(x+2)(x+3)$
$x^2+3x+2x+6$
x^2+5x+6

Example

Factorise $x^2 - 5x + 6$.

Solution

In this case the numbers are -2 and -3.

$$x^2 - 5x + 6 = (x - 2)(x - 3)$$

$(-2) \times (-3) = +6$
$(-2) + (-3) = -5$

This solution is incomplete. What is missing?

1 a) Find two numbers with product 5 and sum 6.

b) Use these numbers to help you factorise $x^2 + 6x + 5$.

c) Check your answer by expanding your brackets.

2 a) Find two numbers with product 15 and sum 8.

b) Use these numbers to help you factorise $y^2 + 8y + 15$.

c) Check your answers by expanding your brackets.

3 Factorise these and check your answers.

a) $x^2 + 9x + 14$ b) $x^2 + 15x + 14$ c) $a^2 + 7a + 10$

d) $a^2 + 11a + 10$ e) $n^2 + 5n + 4$ f) $t^2 + 4t + 4$

g) $x^2 + 4x + 4$ h) $x^2 + 9x + 18$ i) $y^2 + 10y + 24$

4 a) Find two negative numbers with product +5 and sum –6.

b) Use these to help you factorise $x^2 - 6x + 5$.

c) Check your answer by expanding your brackets.

5 a) Find two numbers with product +15 and sum –8.

b) Use these numbers to help you factorise $y^2 - 8y + 15$.

c) Check your answer by expanding your brackets.

6 Factorise these and check your answers.

a) $x^2 - 3x + 2$ b) $x^2 - 4x + 3$ c) $x^2 - 6x + 5$

d) $x^2 - 12x + 11$ e) $x^2 - 9x + 14$ f) $x^2 - 6x + 8$

g) $p^2 - 9p + 18$ h) $a^2 - 15a + 44$ i) $x^2 - 45x + 44$

7 Factorise these and check your answers.

a) $y^2 - 2y + 1$ b) $a^2 + 13a + 22$ c) $x^2 - 10x + 21$

d) $p^2 - 10p + 16$ e) $t^2 - 8t + 12$ f) $y^2 + 7y + 12$

g) $a^2 + 2a + 1$ h) $x^2 + 6x + 9$ i) $y^2 - 4y + 4$

j) $t^2 - 10t + 25$ k) $x^2 - 6x + 9$ l) $y^2 - 5y + 4$

m) $p^2 - 12p + 36$ n) $x^2 + 14x + 49$ o) $x^2 - 25x + 100$

More quadratic factorisation

In quadratics you have factorised so far the number terms have been positive (+). When you factorised these you got two brackets with the same signs inside, such as $(x-3)(x-2)$ or $(x+5)(x+2)$.

In the examples on this page the number term is negative (–), and you have to be a bit more careful with the signs.

Look at $x^2 - x - 20$.

> Note: $-x$ means $-1x$.

You need to find two numbers that multiply to give –20 and add to give –1.

To multiply to get 20, you can have 20 and 1, 10 and 2 or 5 and 4.

Since it is –20, one of the numbers must be positive and one negative.

After trying the various pairs, you can see that the only one that works is –5 and +4.

The answer is $x^2 - x - 20 = (x-5)(x+4)$.

Check this by multiplying out the brackets.

Copy and complete this table. Look carefully at the pattern of signs in your table.

What signs should you expect in the brackets when you factorise $x^2 - x - 12$?

Brackets	Quadratic
$(x+3)(x+5)$	$x^2 + 8x + 15$
$(x-3)(x-5)$	
$(x-3)(x+5)$	
$(x+3)(x-5)$	

In Chapter 9 you met quadratic expressions like $x^2 - 9$ (the difference of two squares). You can factorise $x^2 - 9$ by writing it as $x^2 - 0x - 9$.

Work this through to get the answer $(x+3)(x-3)$.

Use the same idea to factorise $x^2 - 4$.

It is useful to remember that $x^2 - a^2$ factorises to $(x+a)(x-a)$.

When you need to factorise a quadratic expression whose terms have a common factor, you take out the common factor first.

Example $2x^2 + 6x + 2$

> The terms have a common factor 2.

$= 2(x^2 + 3x + 2)$

$= 2(x+1)(x+2)$

1 a) Think of two numbers with product 6 and and difference 5.

    b) Use these to help you factorise $x^2 + 5x - 6$.

    c) Factorise $x^2 - 5x - 6$.

Check your answers by expanding the brackets.

2 a) Think of two numbers with product 15 and difference 2.

    b) Use these to help you factorise $y^2 + 2y - 15$.

    c) Factorise $y^2 - 2y - 15$.

Check your answers by expanding the brackets.

3 Factorise these and check your answers.

    a) $x^2 + 10x - 11$ b) $x^2 - 10x - 11$ c) $x^2 + 6x - 7$

    d) $x^2 - 6x - 7$ e) $x^2 + 4x - 5$ f) $x^2 - 4x - 5$

    g) $x^2 + 5x - 14$ h) $x^2 - 5x - 14$ i) $x^2 + 3x - 88$

4 Factorise these and check your answers.

    a) $a^2 + 7a - 18$ b) $a^2 - 7a - 18$ c) $y^2 + 9y - 10$

    d) $y^2 - 3y - 10$ e) $p^2 - 3p - 18$ f) $x^2 - x - 12$

    g) $x^2 + x - 20$ h) $a^2 + 8a - 20$ i) $t^2 + 4t - 12$

5 Factorise these and check your answers.

    a) $x^2 - 4$ b) $y^2 - 25$ c) $z^2 - 1$

    d) $n^2 - 16$ e) $t^2 - 49$ f) $p^2 - 100$

6 Here is a mixture of types to factorise. Check your answers carefully.

    a) $x^2 + 7x + 6$ b) $x^2 + 6x + 8$ c) $r^2 - 5r + 4$

    d) $x^2 - 8x - 9$ e) $y^2 + 3y - 4$ f) $x^2 + x - 12$

    g) $t^2 - t - 12$ h) $x^2 - 11x + 18$ i) $p^2 + 4p - 12$

    j) $y^2 - 81$ k) $b^2 - b - 20$ l) $a^2 - 11a + 10$

7 Factorise these completely.

    a) $4x^2 + 4x - 48$ b) $3a^2 - 9a + 6$ c) $3x^2 - 12$

    d) $3x^2 + 6x + 3$ e) $10x^2 - 1000$ f) $5x^2 + 10x - 400$

Quadratic equations

Look at the equation

$$x^2 - 2x - 15 = 0$$

This is a **quadratic equation**.

 Why is it called a quadratic equation?

To solve a quadratic equation, start by factorising the left-hand side.

$$x^2 - 2x - 15 = 0$$
$$(x - 5)(x + 3) = 0$$

This gives you two factors $(x - 5)$ and $(x + 3)$ that multiply to give 0. One of them must be 0.

Either $x - 5 = 0$ and so $x = 5$

or $x + 3 = 0$ and so $x = -3$.

The solution of the equation is $x = 5$ or -3.

Example

Solve $x(x - 4) = -3$

Solution

First get this equation into the right form.

$$x(x - 4) = -3$$

Expand the brackets $x^2 - 4x = -3$

Add 3 to both sides $x^2 - 4x + 3 = 0$

$$(x - 1)(x - 3) = 0$$

Either $x - 1 = 0$ so $x = 1$

or $x - 3 = 0$ so $x = 3$

The solution is $x = 1$ or 3

You can get the same result by drawing a graph.

This is the graph of

$$y = x^2 - 4x + 3$$

You can see that is crosses the x axis at $x = 1$ and at $x = 3$

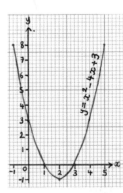

Sometimes you will meet quadratic equations which cannot be factorised.

In such cases, you can still solve the equation by drawing the graph.

However, as you will find out from the Investigation on page 149, some quadratic equations have no solution.

1 Solve these equations.

a) $(x-4)(x-1) = 0$ b) $x(x-4) = 0$ c) $2(x-4) = 0$

d) $x(x+4) = 0$ e) $y(y-3) = 0$ f) $(x-2)(x-3) = 0$

g) $(x-5)(x+3) = 0$ h) $t^2 - 2t = 0$ i) $y^2 + 4y = 0$

2 Solve these equations.

a) $x^2 - 9x + 14 = 0$ b) $a^2 - 7a + 10 = 0$ c) $x^2 + 5x - 14 = 0$

d) $n^2 + 5n + 4 = 0$ e) $a^2 + a - 6 = 0$ f) $t^2 - 4t - 12 = 0$

g) $x^2 + 5x - 50 = 0$ h) $x^2 - 2x - 63 = 0$ i) $x^2 - 12x + 11 = 0$

3 Repeat the steps in question 4 to solve each of these.

a) $x^2 + x = 20$ b) $a^2 + 8a = 20$ c) $r^2 + 4 = 5r$

d) $y^2 - 3y = 4$ e) $x^2 + 18 = -11x$ f) $x^2 = x + 12$

g) $a^2 + 3a = 16 - 3a$ h) $x^2 + 3x = 4 + 3x$ i) $30 + x^2 = 11x$

4 For each of the following situations

(i) form an equation in the unknown quantity given

(ii) solve the equation   (iii) check your answer.

a) The length of a rectangular lawn is 3 m greater than its width, w m. Its area is 54 m^2.

b) The width of a box is 10 cm less than its length, l cm. Its height is 8 cm and its volume is 3000 cm^3.

c) A box has a square base of side x cm and height 2 cm. Its outside surface area (including its top and bottom) is 90 cm^2.

5 a) Make out a table of values and draw the graph of $y = x^2 - x$ for values of x from -4 to 4.

b) Draw the line $y = 6$ on your graph and write down the values of x where the line meets the curve.

c) Solve the equation $x^2 - x = 6$ as in question 4.

d) Explain why your answers to b) and c) should be the same.

e) Use your graph to solve the equation $x^2 - x = 8$.

Is it possible to solve this by factorising?

Investigation

Draw the graphs of

a) $y = x^2 - 6x + 8$ b) $y = x^2 - 6x + 9$ c) $y = x^2 - 6x + 10$

Use them to solve the equations

$$x^2 - 6x + 8 = 0$$
$$x^2 - 6x + 9 = 0$$
$$x^2 - 6x + 10 = 0$$

The equation $x^2 - 6x + k = 0$ has no solution. What can you say about k?

Quadratic sequences

This mystic rose is made by joining each of the 20 points on the circle to every other point. The number of lines involved is very difficult to count, but you can find a method for working it out if you start by considering simpler roses.

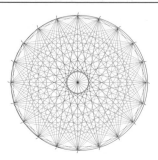

 How many lines are needed to join 2 points on a circle?

What about 3, or 4 points?

In this diagram, 5 points are joined by 10 lines.

 How many extra *lines are needed for a 6th point?*

How many will there be altogether?

Here is how Kevin writes it down.

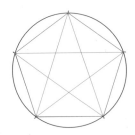

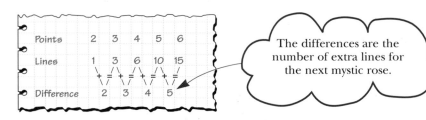

The differences are the number of extra lines for the next mystic rose.

You can see that the number of lines form a sequence: 1, 3, 6, 10, 15, …

The pattern is that the difference increases by 1 each time.

This is what happens with **quadratic sequences**.

Look at the 5-point rose. If you start at each point and join it to the 4 others, you draw $5 \times 4 = 20$ lines but you have drawn each line twice so you only need $\frac{1}{2} \times 5 \times 4 = 10$ lines.

Similarly for a 20-point rose, the total number is $\frac{1}{2} \times 20 \times 19 = 190$

The formula for a rose with n points is $\frac{1}{2} n(n - 1)$

Expanding this gives the quadratic expression $\frac{1}{2} n^2 - \frac{1}{2} n$

Substituting $n = 2, 3, 4, …$ gives the quadratic sequence Kevin found.

 What happens for $n = 1$?

 Work out the number of lines for a 12-point rose using a sequence like Kevin's and also add the formula. Do they give the same answer?

1 Copy each of these sequences and write down the next 3 terms.

   a) $1 \times 3, \quad 2 \times 4, \quad 3 \times 5, \ldots$
   b) $1 \times 2 - 1, \quad 2 \times 3 - 2, \quad 3 \times 4 - 3, \ldots$
   c) $1 \times 5, \quad 2 \times 6, \quad 3 \times 7, \ldots$

2 a) Copy this sequence and write down the next 3 terms.

   $1, 4, 9, 16, 25, \ldots$

   b) Write down a formula for the nth term.

   c) Write down another row showing the differences between the terms in the sequence in part a).

   d) Continue the sequence for 3 more terms using the differences and check that your formula in b) is still correct.

3 a) Copy and complete this table for a sequence of numbers.

Term number	1	2	3	4	5	6
Term	1×2	2×3	3×4			

   b) The third term is $3 \times (3 + 1)$. Write a formula for the nth term.

4 a) Copy this sequence and write down the next 3 terms.

   $1 \times 0 + 1, \quad 2 \times 1 + 2, \quad 3 \times 2 + 3, \quad 4 \times 3 + 4, \ldots$

   b) Write down a formula for the nth term.

   c) Work out the values of the first 4 terms of the sequence. Use these values to suggest a different formula for the nth term.

   d) Simplify your first formula to show that they are both the same.

Investigation

For Sylvia and Ted's first Christmas, there are just the two of them. They give each other a present, making 2 presents in all.

By the next Christmas, baby Fiona has arrived. As well as giving each other presents, they each give Fiona one, and they buy presents for Fiona to give to each of them. There are 6 presents.

Two years later, Fiona's brother Jack has arrived. How many Christmas presents are now given?

They go on having children. How does the number of presents increase with the number of children?

One year the family has to buy 90 presents. How many children are there then?

How is this situation related to the mystic rose?

Finishing off

Now that you have finished this chapter you should be able to

★ factorise quadratic expressions

★ solve quadratic equations

★ find terms in quadratic sequences.

Use the questions in the next exercise to check that you understand everything.

Mixed exercise

1 Factorise each of these and check your answers.

a) $x^2 + 13x + 12$ b) $a^2 - 3a + 2$

c) $z^2 - 6z + 8$ d) $n^2 + 11n - 26$

e) $t^2 - 4t - 12$ f) $x^2 - 7x - 30$

2 Factorise each of these and check your answers.

a) $x^2 + 2x + 1$ b) $n^2 - 10n + 25$

c) $r^2 + 8r + 16$ d) $y^2 - 12y + 36$

e) $x^2 - 16$ f) $p^2 - 49$

3 Solve each of these equations and check your answers.

a) $2x = 0$ b) $3(x + 2) = 0$ c) $x(x - 2) = 0$

d) $a(a + 15) = 0$ e) $(t - 5)(t + 6) = 0$ f) $(a + 7)(a + 11) = 0$

g) $(x - 3)(x + 3) = 0$ h) $(2n - 3)(3n - 9) = 0$ i) $2(y - 5)(3y - 2) = 0$

4 Solve each of these equations and check your answers.

a) $x^2 - 5x + 6 = 0$ b) $b^2 + 7b + 12 = 0$ c) $x^2 + 18x + 81 = 0$

d) $x^2 + 3x - 18 = 0$ e) $d^2 - 4d - 21 = 0$ f) $x^2 - 10x - 24 = 0$

g) $x^2 + 2x = 0$ h) $n^2 - 4 = 0$ i) $3x^2 - 12 = 0$

5 Solve each of these equations and check your answers.

a) $x^2 - x = 56$ b) $x^2 + x = 90$ c) $y = y^2 - 12$

d) $t^2 + 6 = 5t$ e) $n^2 = 14 - 5n$ f) $x^2 = 3(6 - x)$

g) $x^2 = 20 + x$ h) $x^2 = 5x$ i) $2x^2 = 20x - 42$

6 For the sequence $0 \times 2, \ 1 \times 3, \ 2 \times 4, \ 3 \times 5, \ldots$

a) write down the 5th term

b) use brackets to write down a formula for the nth term

c) work out the first 5 terms and so find a different formula for the nth term

d) Show that your answers to parts b) and c) are the same.

7 For the sequence 1×2, 2×3, 3×4, ...

a) write down the next three terms

b) write down a formula for the nth term

c) The nth term is 56. Write a quadratic equation for n and solve it to find n.

8 A number of teams play in a tennis league.

a) How many matches are required if there are 4 teams and each team plays all the others twice? (You might find a diagram helpful.)

b) Copy and complete this table showing the number of matches for 2, 3, 4, 5 and 6 teams.

Teams	2	3	4	5	6
Matches	2	6			
Differences		4			

c) Compare this with Kevin's diagram on page 150 for the mystic rose.

How many matches are required for 20 teams and for n teams?

d) Use an equation to find out how many teams are in the league if a total of 110 matches are played.

9 A rectangular garden is x metres by $x + 2$ metres. It has paths and flower beds one metre wide round the edge with a lawn in the middle.

a) Draw a diagram of the garden, showing all the measurements clearly.

b) Write down the dimensions of the lawn in terms of x and find an expression for its area.

c) The lawn requires 120 m^2 of turf. Write down an equation for x.

d) Solve your equation to find x. What are the dimensions of the garden?

Design an exhibition space for showing paintings using 16 m of screens. Describe what you intend to exhibit and your reasons for using the screens as you have.

Draw a plan of your space showing any other furniture you might need.

Fourteen

Transformations

Use this exercise to check that you remember these topics.

Revision exercise

1 a) Which of the triangles in this diagram are congruent to A?

b) Which of the triangles are congruent to B?

c) Describe the transformations which map

   (i) I → A   (ii) C → D   (iii) E → F

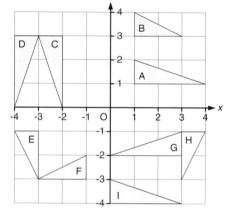

2 The shape P is formed by joining the points

   $(0, 0)$, $(5, 0)$, $(5, 2)$, $(3\frac{1}{2}, 3\frac{1}{2})$

a) Draw P on graph paper. Use the same scales for both x and y. You will need values between −5 and 5 on both axes.

Now draw the following transformations of P.

b) R, T and V are rotations of P with centre O through 90°, 180° and 270° anticlockwise respectively.

c) W and S are reflections of P in the x and y axes.

d) Q and U are reflections of P in the lines $y = x$ and $y = -x$.

e) You have now drawn 8 congruent shapes which together make a polygon.

Describe this polygon, and state what symmetry it has.

Revision exercise

3 Professor Kandola is an expert on beetles. She finds a type she has never seen before on a remote island. She places them on a notebook and photographs them before releasing them. She notices that there are two patterns on their backs. She calls A 'Dexter' and B 'Sinister'.

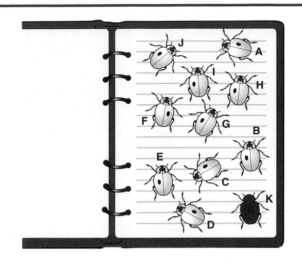

a) What is the difference between Dexter and Sinister?

b) Which other beetles are type Dexter and which Sinister?

c) One of the beetles is on its back. Professor Kandola's assistant says 'If it rolls one way to get up it will be a Dexter and if it rolls the other way it will be a Sinister'. Is he right?

4 The diagram shows shapes F and G.

a) Describe the enlargement which maps F → G.

b) Describe the enlargement which maps G → F.

Shape H is an enlargement of F with centre (2,0) scale factor 3.

c) Draw F, G and H on graph paper.

d) State the transformation which maps H → G.

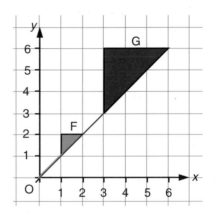

Make two different tessellations using this chevron shape. (Each of them must have at the very least 10 copies of the shape.) Are there other ways you can tessellate this shape?

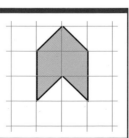

Combining transformations

This diagram shows part of a repeating pattern. It is made out of transformations of triangle A.

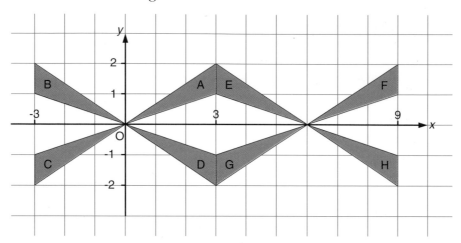

 You can map A onto each of B, C, D, E, F and G by a single transformation. In each case it is either a reflection or a rotation or a translation. How would you describe these six transformations?

When you come to H, you find that there is no single transformation. You need two. One way of doing this is

First rotate A centre (0, 0) through 180° then do a reflection in the vertical line *x* = 3.

 How many more ways can you find to map A → H in two steps? Remember to be careful to say which of the two comes first and which second.

Here is a real-life example of combining transformations.

The diagram shows a 400 m running track.

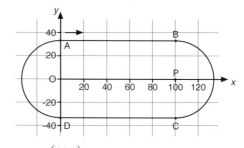

An athlete starts at point A, (0, 32) and runs round the track in a clockwise direction.

Running from A to B involves a translation $\begin{pmatrix} 100 \\ 0 \end{pmatrix}$ and from B to C a rotation centre P (100, 0) through 180°.

 What transformations represent the athlete's run from C back to A? Which of the four transformations cancel each other out? Can the athlete have a reflection?

Exercise

Questions 1–4 of this exercise refer to the triangles in this diagram.

1 Describe the transformations which map

a) (i) A → D (ii) D → E (iii) A → E

b) (i) A → D (ii) D → M (iii) A → M

c) Is it possible for 2 reflections to be the same as
   (i) a translation
   (ii) a rotation
   (iii) another reflection?

2 Describe the transformations which map

a) (i) A → I (ii) I → J (iii) A → J

b) Is it possible for 2 translations to be the same as
   (i) another translation
   (ii) a rotation through 90°
   (iii) a reflection?

3 Describe the transformations which map

a) (i) A → K (ii) K → L

b) (i) A → C (ii) C → L

c) Is there a single transformation which maps A → L?

4 Give examples using the triangles in the diagram, to show that

a) two rotations are equivalent to another rotation.

b) the same reflection carried out twice cancels itself out.

The diagram shows a settee in one corner of a room (position A) which has to be turned round and moved to the opposite corner (position B). The settee has legs at its four corners. It is too heavy to lift or slide and so has to be rotated about one of its legs.

Copy the diagram and shade, in different colours, the moves needed to get the settee to its new position. Mark in the centre of each rotation.

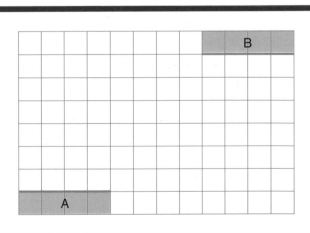

Applying transformations to graphs

This is the graph of $y = x^2$.

Sometimes you will need to draw a graph with an equation that is nearly, but not quite, the same as one you know. You can think of this as a transformation.

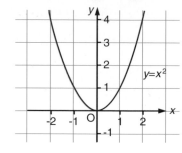

The graph of $y = x^2 + 2$ is a translation by $\begin{pmatrix} 0 \\ 2 \end{pmatrix}$ of $y = x^2$.

You can think of it as adding 2 to the value of y at every point.

Is the line $y = x + 4$ a translation by $\begin{pmatrix} 0 \\ 4 \end{pmatrix}$ of $y = x$?

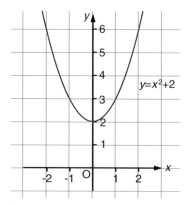

The graph of $y = -x^2$ is the reflection of $y = x^2$ in the x axis.

Does a minus sign always cause a reflection in the x-axis? Try it on some other curves and lines.

The graph below shows the curves $y = x^2$ and $y = (x - 3)^2$. Describe the transformation that maps $y = x^2$ onto this curve.

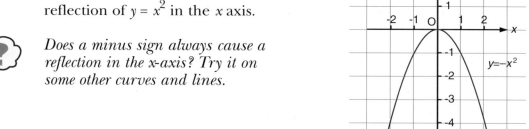

The transformation that maps $y = x^2$ onto $y = 2x^2$ is one that you have not met before. Plot the curve and describe this transformation in your own words.

1 The equation of the red curve in the diagram is $y = \dfrac{6}{x}$. It is shown for values of x between 1 and 6.

The diagram also shows the curves with equations

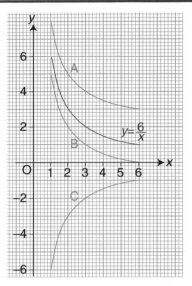

1. $y = \dfrac{6}{x} - 1$

2. $y = -\dfrac{6}{x}$

3. $y = \dfrac{6}{x} + 2$

Say which of the curves A, B and C has which equation.

2 a) Make out a table of values, taking $x = -3$, 0 and 3, for each of

    (i) $y = x$ (ii) $y = x + 2$ (iii) $y = x - 3$ (iv) $y = -x$

b) Draw the four graphs, using the same axes. Use a scale of 1 cm to 1 unit on both axes and label each graph with its equation.

c) Describe the transformations which map $y = x$ onto each of the other three graphs.

3 a) Draw the graph of $y = x^2$ taking values of x from -2 to 2.

b) Draw the graph of $y = x^2 + 3$ on the same piece of graph paper. Describe the transformation which maps $y = x^2$ onto $y = x^2 + 3$.

c) Draw the graph of $y = -(x^2 + 3)$. Describe the transformations which map

    (i) $y = x^2 + 3$ onto $y = -(x^2 + 3)$ (ii) $y = x^2$ onto $y = -(x^2 + 2)$.

This should be done on graph paper. Mark the origin near the middle of the sheet and take values from -9 to $+9$ and use the same scale on both axes.

Draw the line joining (0, 8) to (1, 0) and also the three transformations of the line given by reflecting it in the x axis, reflecting it in the y axis and rotating it through 180° about the origin. Now do the same for the lines joining (0, 7) to (2, 0), (0, 6) to (3, 0), and so on.

Describe your complete diagram.

Finishing off

Now that you have finished this chapter you should be able to

★ investigate situations involving two transformations

★ recognise how transformations can be applied to graphs.

Use this exercise and earlier work on transformations to check that you understand everything.

1 A triangle A has co-ordinates $(0, 0)$, $(1, 0)$, $(3, 3)$.

a) Draw triangle A, using the same scale for both x and y axes. Take values between -3 and $+3$ for both x and y.

b) Triangles B, C and D are formed by rotating A anticlockwise about O through $90°$, $180°$ and $270°$, respectively. Draw, B, C and D.

c) Triangles E, F, G and H are formed by reflecting A, B, C and D in the x axis. Draw E, F, G and H.

d) Describe single transformations which map

(i) A → G (ii) A → H.

2 Answer this question on graph paper. Use the same scale for the x axis (values -4 to 12) and the y axis (values 0 to 12).

A triangle L has co-ordinates $(4, 3)$, $(6, 3)$, $(6, 4)$.
Another triangle P has co-ordinates $(0, 6)$, $(4, 6)$, $(4, 8)$.

a) Find the centre of the enlargement which maps L onto P, and the scale factor.

b) Triangle P is given a translation $\begin{pmatrix} 4 \\ 0 \end{pmatrix}$ to form triangle Q, and a translation $\begin{pmatrix} 8 \\ 0 \end{pmatrix}$ to form R. Find the centres of the enlargements which map L onto Q and R.

c) Triangle L is now enlarged from the same three centres but with scale factor 3. Do the enlarged triangles touch each other, like P, Q and R do?

3 The diagram shows an equilateral triangle A. Copy it onto graph paper.

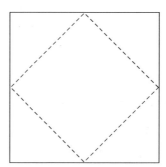

a) On the same diagram as A, draw triangle B which is formed by rotating A through 60° anticlockwise about O.

b) Add in triangles C, D, E and F formed by rotating A through 120°, 180°, 240° and 300° about O.

c) Describe the complete shape you have now drawn.

d) Is it possible to draw the same shape starting with A and doing reflections in the *x* axis and reflections in the *y* axis?

e) Describe how you can draw the same shape starting with A and doing translations and reflections in the *x* axis.

4 a) Make a table of values for the curve $y = x^3$ taking *x* from −2 to +2. Draw the curve on graph paper.

b) Without doing any more calculations, use your curve to draw the graphs of
(i) $y = x^3 + 2$ (ii) $y = x^3 - 1$ (iii) $y = -x^3$

Investigation

Take a square sheet of paper and fold it twice along the lines joining the middle points of its sides (the dotted lines in the diagram). You will find it gives you another, smaller square. You can then fold that to make a smaller square, and so on…

Find another shape that you can keep folding on itself.

If you want to make a single sheet of paper into a 4-sided leaflet you must number it like this:

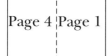

Side 1 | Page 4 | Page 1   Side 2 | Page 2 | Page 3

How can you lay out the page to make a single sheet of paper into an 8-page booklet? Where do you have to make cuts in the paper?

Fifteen

Finance

Before you start this chapter you should be able to

★ work out simple interest

★ work out wages, commission and taxation

★ work out household bills

★ work out the costs of 'buy now, pay later' deals

★ work out VAT

★ calculate profit or loss.

Use the questions in the next exercise to check that you still remember these topics.

Revision exercise

1 Work out the simple interest on

a) £300 invested at 5% p.a. for 1 year

b) £2500 invested at 15% p.a. for 3 years

c) £6000 invested at 2.75% p.a. for 4 years

d) £18 400 invested at 11.4% p.a. for 6 years.

2 Work out how much each person earns a week.

a) Pamal earns £6.20 an hour and works 35 hours a week.

b) Jean earns £7.80 an hour for a 32 hour week. She decides to work on Saturday and does 6 hours overtime at 'time and a half'.

c) Barry earns £4.20 an hour for a 38 hour week. He does 8 hours overtime at 'double time'.

3 Sarah's gross (before tax) salary is £22 600. She has a tax-free allowance of £4600. She pays tax at 26p in the pound.

a) Calculate how much tax she pays.

b) Calculate her net (after tax) income.

She receives a 14% pay rise. Her allowance remains the same.

c) What is her new gross salary?

d) Calculate her new net income.

e) Calculate the increase in her net income.

4 Lynn wants to take a taxi from the centre of London to Heathrow Airport (a distance of 30 miles). She finds out the fares from two taxi companies.

Calculate the cost of the journey using each of the companies.

5 All of these prices are excluding VAT. Work out the cost including VAT at 17.5%.

a) £480   b) £350   c) £6900   d) £7224   e) £12 226

6 Calculate the percentage profit or loss on an item

a) bought for £30 and sold for £42

b) bought for £1230 and sold for £1414.50

c) bought for £48 and sold for £36

d) bought for £75 and sold for £52.50.

7 Work out the selling price of an item

a) bought for £620 and sold at a 15% profit

b) bought for £35 and sold at a 22% profit

c) bought for £224 and sold at a 16% loss

d) bought for £8246 and sold at a 11% loss.

8 Peter is a market trader. He buys 20 shirts at £12 each. He prices them so that he makes a 40% profit on each shirt.

a) What price does he charge for each shirt?

b) He sells 14 of them at this price and the remainder are sold for £10.

How much does he take altogether?

c) What is his total profit?

d) Work out this profit as a percentage of his total outlay.

Go to a bank or building society. Find out the rates of interest they offer for their different accounts.

Which account would you choose if you had £100 to invest?

What if you had £10 000 to invest?

Compound interest

George puts £400 in this building society.

This stands for 'per annum' or per year

BUILDING SOCIETY

TopHat

Platinum Savings Account

10% p.a. interest

How much money does he have after 3 years?

Building societies and banks usually pay interest straight into your account.

At the end of the first year, George gets the interest on his £400.

At the end of the second year, he gets the interest on his £400 and on the interest he got last year. This is the **compound** interest.

This is how George's money increases over 3 years.

After 1 year:

$\text{Interest} = \dfrac{10}{100} \times £400 = £40$

Amount at the end of year = £400 + £40 = £440

After 2 years:

$\text{Interest} = \dfrac{10}{100} \times £440 = £44$

Amount at end of year = £440 + £44 = £484

After 3 years:

$\text{Interest} = \dfrac{10}{100} \times £484 = £48.40$

Amount at end of year = £484 + £48.40 = £532.40

After 3 years, George has £532.40 in his account.

How much would George have if the building society paid simple interest (interest just on the original £400)?

Would you prefer simple or compound interest?

1 Calculate the compound interest on

a) £200 invested at 10% p.a. for 3 years

b) £1000 invested at 5% p.a. for 2 years

c) £150 invested at 6% p.a. for 2 years

d) £14 500 invested at 9% p.a. for 3 years

e) £22 420 invested at 8% p.a. for 4 years

f) £6 200 invested at 7.5% p.a. for 2 years.

2 Jan invests £1500 in a bank account that pays interest at 6% p.a.

How much does she have after 3 years if the bank pays

a) simple interest?

b) compound interest?

3 Andy invests £800 in a building society account that pays compound interest at 8% p.a.

Copy and complete this chart which shows details of his account over 5 years.

Year	Amount at start of year	Interest	Amount at end of year
1	£800	£800 × $\frac{8}{100}$ = £64	£800 + £64 = £864
2	£864	£864 × $\frac{8}{100}$ =	
3			
4			
5			

4 Tessa has £1200 to invest. She sees these adverts.

How much does Tessa have after 2 years if she invests in

a) the bank?

b) the building society?

c) Tessa decides to invest in the bank. How long does she have to leave the money in this account before this becomes a bad decision?

Gray Bank

simple interest

7% p.a.

Austin and Pearson Building Society

6·5% p.a. COMPOUND INTEREST

Insurance

Usma has damaged her car. No one is hurt but she needs to get it repaired.

It will be expensive to repair the car, but Usma has car **insurance**

She pays the insurance company a certain amount every year. In return, they pay to repair her car if she has an accident.

The amount Usma pays each year is called her **insurance premium**

She gets a discount on her insurance premium called a no claims bonus. For every year, up to 3 years, that she does not make a claim she gets a discount of 20%.

Years without claim	No claims bonus
0	0%
1	20%
2	40%
3	60%

What percentage will Usma's no claims bonus be next year?

Usma's friend Rob has not made a claim for 2 years. His insurance premium before the no claims bonus is £500.

His no claims bonus is 40% of £500.

$$\frac{40}{100} \times \frac{500}{1} = 200$$

So his no claims bonus is £200.

His insurance premium after his no claims bonus is

£500 − £200 = £300

Rob drives for a further year without a claim. What is his insurance premium after his no claims bonus has been taken off?

1 Work out the insurance premium of these people after their no claims bonus has been taken off. Use the table on the opposite page.

a) Rick's insurance premium is £380.
   He has not made a claim for 2 years.

b) Graham's insurance premium is £480.
   He made a claim last month.

c) Claire's insurance premium is £510.
   She has not made a claim for 1 year.

d) Brennan's insurance premium is £280.
   He has not made a claim for 8 years.

2 A health insurance company uses this table of insurance premiums.

	Female	Male
Age (years)	**Cost per month (£)**	**Cost per month (£)**
under 16	17.50	18.40
16–25	15.70	16.50
26–35	17.95	19.80
36–45	18.80	20.70
46–55	21.20	22.15
56–65	23.80	24.80
66+	25.15	26.20

Add on 10% for smokers

What are the insurance premiums per month for each of the following people?

a) Harold, a 65 year-old smoker.

b) Sylvia, a 43 year-old non-smoker.

c) Mick, a 27 year-old smoker.

d) Daphne, an 18 month-old baby.

e) Why are these insurance premiums for smokers higher than the insurance premiums for non-smokers?

Apart from those mentioned in this chapter, there are many other types of insurance.

Find out six other types of insurance.

Finding the original price

Peter has a clothes stall on the market.

He sells all of his stock at 40% profit.

 How much did he pay for this sweater?

Peter has added 40% so

> 140% of the cost price is £49
>
> 1% of the cost price = $\dfrac{£49}{140}$ = £0.35
>
> 100% of the cost price = £0.35 × 100 = £35

Peter bought the sweater for £35.

'Jasmine's Jacket Shop' is having a sale.

How much did this jacket cost before the sale?

The jacket costs 25% less in the sale, so it is

> 100% − 25% = 75% of the original price
>
> 75% of the original price = £60
>
> 1% of the original price = $\dfrac{£60}{75}$ = £0.80
>
> 100% of the original price = £0.80 × 100 = £80

The jacket cost £80 before the sale.

 Another jacket costs £81 in the sale. What did it cost before the sale?

1 The price of a monthly train ticket increases by 12% to £84.

What did it cost before the increase?

2 Richard is given a 16% pay rise. His salary is £29 232.

What was his salary before the rise?

3 Sarah sees this sign.

She pays £596.40 for a computer in the sale.

a) What was the original price of the computer?

b) How much does she save?

4 Marco is buying some furniture for his new flat.

The prices include 17.5% VAT.

Work out the price of each item excluding VAT.

5 Ryan buys a washing machine. He pays 12 monthly instalments of £34.

a) How much does he pay in total?

b) Ryan had to pay 20% more than the original shop price because he paid by instalments.

Work out the original shop price.

6 Zoe sells her car for £5170. She makes a 6% loss on the original price.

How much did Zoe originally pay for the car?

Find a list of second hand car prices.

Work out the percentage yearly loss in value for different cars.

Finishing off

Now that you have finished this chapter you should be able to

★ calculate compound interest

★ calculate insurance premiums from tables

★ calculate the original price after a percentage increase or decrease.

Use the questions in the next exercise to check that you understand everything.

1 Calculate the compound interest on

a) £600 invested at 7% p.a. for 2 years

b) £20 000 invested at 12% for 5 years

c) £1250 invested at 8% p.a. for 3 years

d) £6050 invested at 5.5% p.a. for 4 years.

2 Joe invests £500 in Buckton Building Society.

At the same time, Mary invests £500 in Woodbridge Building Society.

a) After 2 years, how much interest has

(i) Joe earned?

(ii) Mary earned?

b) How many years is it before Mary has more in her account than Joe?

3 Naseem invests £1000 in a building society account which pays compound interest at 7% p.a.

Copy and complete this table which shows the details of his account over 5 years.

Year	Amount at start of year	Interest	Amount at end of year
1	£1000	£1000 × 7/100 = £70	£100 + £70 = £1070
2	£1070	£1070 × 7/100 =	
3			
4			
5			

4 This table shows the insurance premiums of a travel insurance company.

Length of holiday (days)	Destination				
	UK	Europe	North America	South America	Asia
1–7	£9	£17	£18	£21	£24
8–21	£16.20	£30.60	£32.40	£37.80	£43.20
22–84	£29.16	£55.08	£58.32	£68.04	£77.76
85–168	£52.49	£99.14	£104.98	£122.47	£139.97

Work out the insurance premiums for each of these people.

a) Julia is travelling to North America for 2 weeks.

b) Alev is travelling to Europe for a weekend.

c) Michael is travelling through Asia for 5 months.

5 Stephen gets a 5% pay rise. His new salary is £17 282.

What was his salary before?

6 Work out the original price of each of these items.

SALE !
Everything has been
reduced by 25%!

SALE PRICE £261.75

SALE PRICE £63

SALE PRICE £149.25

7 a) Emma sells her house for £146 400 at a 22% profit. How much did she pay for it?

b) Peter sells a jacket for £120 at a 40% profit.

How much did he pay for it?

c) Julie sells her exercise bike for £64 at a 20% loss.

How much did she pay for it?

8 The local travel agent has increased the price of all holidays by 6% since last year.

a) Ravi paid £900 for his holiday last year.

How much is the same holiday this year?

b) June paid £420 for her holiday last year.

How much is the same holiday this year?

c) Hannah goes on the same holiday she went on last year.

The new cost of her holiday is £689.

What did she pay last year?

d) David goes on the same holiday he went on last year.

It costs him £60 more than it did last year.

(i) What did he pay last year?

(ii) What does he pay this year?

9 Kerry is a telephone salesperson. She earns a basic salary of £200 per month and gets 12% commission on her sales.

These are her sales figures for January to June.

January	February	March	April	May	June
£4000	£4250	£3600	£4800	£4400	£5200

a) Calculate her total pay for each month.

b) How much does she earn in total over the six months?

c) Kerry's company offers her the chance to change the way she is paid. She can choose from:

> **Option A:** A basic salary of £750 per month (no commission)

> **Option B:** A basic salary of £150 per month plus 15% commission.

Use the sales figures above to work out how much she would have been paid using

(i) Option A

(ii) Option B

d) What would you advise Kerry to choose?

Car insurance companies offer a no claims bonus.

Health insurance companies sometimes offer a non-smokers discount.

Find out some other discounts offered by different types of insurance company.

Think of a city you would like to visit. Look at some timetables and brochures to find out all the different ways to get there from where you live.

Work out the average speed for each of these different ways. (Look back at page 140 if you have forgotten how!)

Is it always more expensive to go faster?

Sixteen

Perimeter, area and volume

Before you start this chapter you should

★ understand the work in Chapter 5 of Intermediate Book 1.

Perimeter and area

Perimeter is the distance round a shape.

You can find the perimeter of any shape with straight edges by adding up the lengths of all the sides.

Area is the amount of space inside a two-dimensional shape. It is measured in square units, such as cm^2 or m^2.

The basic formula for area is the area of a rectangle.

$$\textbf{Area of a rectangle = length} \times \textbf{width}$$

Here are three more useful formulae.

Area of a triangle $= \dfrac{1}{2} \times$ **base** $\times$ **height**

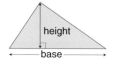

Area of a parallelogram = base $\times$ **height**

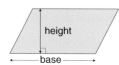

Area of a trapezium $= \dfrac{1}{2}(a + b)h$

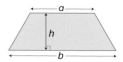

How can you use the formula for the area of a rectangle to find the other three formulae?

The perimeter of a circle is called the circumference. Here are the formulae for the circumference and area of a circle.

$$\textbf{Circumference of circle} = \pi \times \textbf{diameter}$$
$$= \mathbf{2} \times \pi \times \textbf{radius}$$

$$\textbf{Area of circle} = \pi \times \textbf{(radius)}^2$$

1 Find the perimeter and area of each of these shapes.

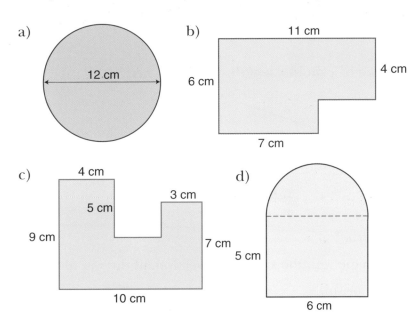

a)

12 cm

b)

11 cm

6 cm

4 cm

7 cm

c)

4 cm

5 cm

3 cm

9 cm

7 cm

10 cm

d)

5 cm

6 cm

2 Find the perimeter and area of each of these shapes. You will need to use Pythagoras' rule to find some of the lengths of the sides.

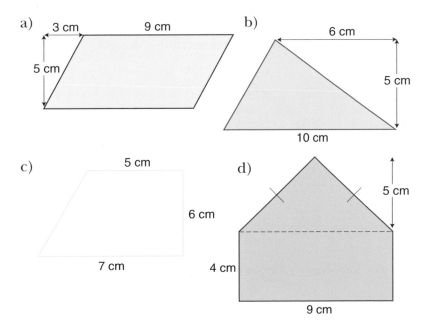

a)

3 cm   9 cm

5 cm

b)

6 cm

5 cm

10 cm

c)

5 cm

6 cm

7 cm

d)

5 cm

4 cm

9 cm

3 Janet has 12 m of chicken wire which she is using to make a circular pen for her rabbit.

a) What is the radius of the pen?

b) What is the area of the pen?

Volume

Volume is the amount of space inside a three-dimensional shape. It is measured in cubic units, such as cm^3 and m^3.

Here are some useful formulae.

Volume of cuboid = length $\times$ width $\times$ height

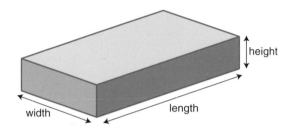

 Why is this formula true?

A **prism** is a solid shape with the same cross-section all the way along it.

A cuboid is a simple prism.
Here is another one.

Volume of prism = area of cross-section $\times$ length

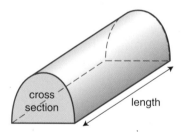

 Why is this formula true?

A **cylinder** is a prism with a circular cross-section.

Volume of cylinder = $\pi r^2 h$

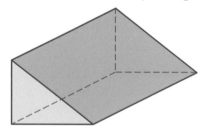

 Why is this formula a special case of the prism formula?

1 Find the volume of each of the solid shapes shown below.

a)

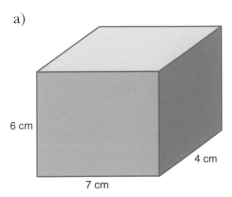

6 cm

4 cm

7 cm

b)

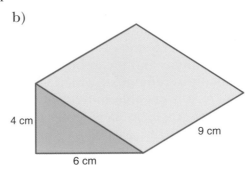

4 cm

9 cm

6 cm

c)

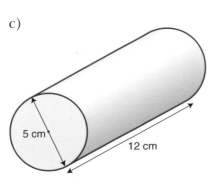

5 cm

12 cm

d)

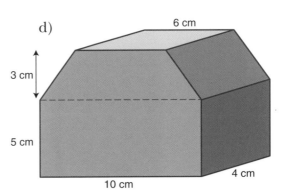

6 cm

3 cm

5 cm

10 cm

4 cm

e)

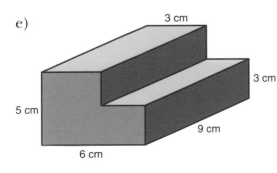

3 cm

3 cm

5 cm

9 cm

6 cm

f)

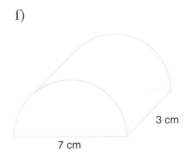

3 cm

7 cm

2 A measuring cylinder is marked in 20 ml increments. The marks are 1 cm apart. Find the radius of the cylinder.

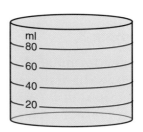

ml
80
60
40
20

Design two different cartons, one a cuboid and the other a cylinder, to hold 500 ml of orange juice. Which shape do you think is better?

Using dimensions

You have now met quite a lot of different formulae for lengths, areas and volumes. There are many more! Some of them are quite similar and it can be difficult to remember which is which. It is possible to tell just by looking at a formula whether it is

$$2\pi r \qquad \pi r^2 h$$
$$lbh \qquad 2l+2h$$
$$\tfrac{1}{2}(a+b)h \qquad \pi r^2$$

for a length, an area or a volume. The way you can tell is by deciding how many **dimensions** there are in it. This means the number of length measurements that have been multiplied together. Numbers, like 2 or π or $\frac{1}{2}$, don't count, because they aren't measurements of length.

- Lengths have one dimension

- Areas have two dimensions

- Volumes have three dimensions.

Example 1

> l, b and h are all measurements of length. The three measurements are multiplied together

$$lbh$$

The formula has **three** dimensions. So this formula is a **volume**.

 What shape has the formula Volume = lbh?

Example 2

> π is not a measurement so it is not a dimension

$$\pi r^2$$

> r^2 counts as two dimensions as it means $r \times r$

The formula has two dimensions. So this formula is an area.

 What shape has the formula Area = πr^2?

Example 3

In some formulae there are two or more parts added together. Each part must have the same number of dimensions. The number of dimensions of the whole formula is the same as the number of dimensions of each part.

> $2l$ has one dimension

$$2l+2h$$

> $2h$ has one dimension

The formula has one dimension. So this formula is a length.

 What shape has the formula Perimeter = $2l + 2h$?

1 Each of these formulae is either a length (perimeter or circumference), area or volume of one of the shapes shown below. For each formula:

a) say how many dimensions it has and what they are
   (Example: $3a^2b$ has three dimensions, a, a and b)

b) say whether the formula is a length, area or volume

c) say which of the shapes A – F it belongs to.

(i) x^2y (ii) $2(x + y)$ (iii) πy^2 (iv) xy

(v) $\frac{1}{2}y(x + y)$ (vi) πx^2y (vii) $\frac{1}{2}xy$ (viii) $2\pi y$

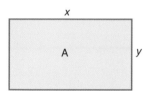

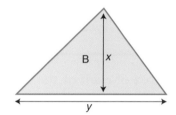

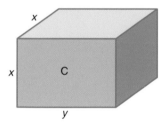

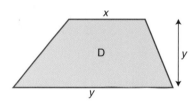

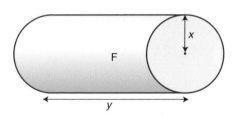

2 Some of the formulae below are real formulae for length, area or volume. Some could not be real formulae because they have the wrong number of dimensions. For each formula, write down whether it is a length, an area, a volume or not a real formula. r, h, a and b are all measurements of length. Any other letters used are not.

a) $\frac{1}{3}\pi r^2h$ b) $2(ah + bh + ab)$ c) $4a + 2b$ d) $2\pi rh + 2\pi r^2$

e) πr^2a^2 f) $\frac{1}{2}ab \sin C$ g) $2r^2 + a^2b$ h) $\frac{4}{3}\pi r^3$

Finishing off

Now that you have finished this chapter you should be able to

★ find perimeters and areas of shapes including rectangles, triangles, parallelograms, trapezia and circles

★ find volumes of solid shapes including cuboids, prisms and cylinders

★ distinguish between formulae for length, area and volume by using dimensions.

Use the questions in the next exercise to check that you understand everything.

Mixed exercise

1 Find the perimeter and area of each of the shapes shown below.

a)
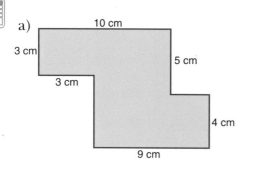

b)
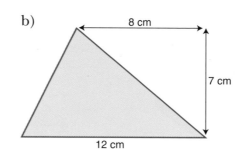

c)
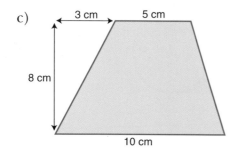

d)
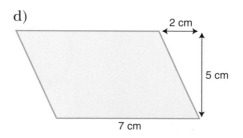

2 A circular garden pond has a diameter of 3.6 m.

a) Find the area of the pond.

b) A fence is put round the pond. How long is the fence?

3 A pipe is 50 m long and holds a volume of 250 litres. Find the radius of the pipe.
(Hint: you may find it easier to work in cm.)

4 Find the volume of each of these solid shapes.

a)

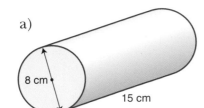

8 cm
15 cm

b)

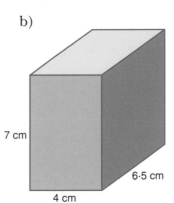

7 cm
6·5 cm
4 cm

c)

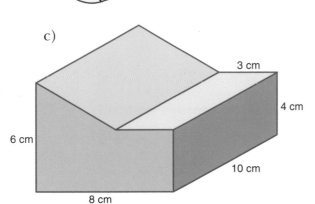

3 cm
4 cm
6 cm
10 cm
8 cm

5 This greenhouse has a capacity of 300 cubic feet. Find the total height of the greenhouse.

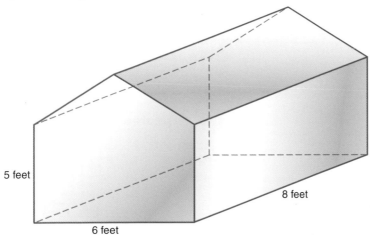

5 feet
8 feet
6 feet

6 For each formula, say whether it is a formula for length, area, volume or none of these. The letters p, q, r and h are all measurements of length.

a) $3pq^2$ b) πrh c) pr^2h d) $\pi(p + q)$

e) $p^2r + qh$ f) πr^3 g) $r(p + q)$

Answers

Chapter 1: Fractions, decimals and percentages

Pages 4–5: Revision exercise

1 Badminton $\frac{1}{2}$, Football $\frac{1}{4}$, Gym $\frac{1}{8}$, Yoga $\frac{1}{8}$

2 a) $2\frac{3}{4}$ b) $2\frac{1}{6}$ c) $3\frac{5}{8}$ d) $4\frac{2}{3}$ e) $3\frac{1}{7}$ f) $3\frac{3}{5}$

3 a) $\frac{13}{4}$ b) $\frac{31}{8}$ c) $\frac{27}{10}$ d) $\frac{17}{3}$ e) $\frac{37}{5}$ f) $\frac{77}{16}$

4 a) $3\frac{1}{2}$ b) $5\frac{1}{8}$ c) $1\frac{5}{16}$ d) $1\frac{9}{16}$ e) $1\frac{3}{16}$

   f) $6\frac{1}{8}$ g) $2\frac{7}{8}$ h) $4\frac{1}{6}$ i) $2\frac{1}{3}$ j) $7\frac{1}{2}$

   k) $1\frac{1}{2}$ l) $7\frac{17}{20}$

5 a) $\frac{51}{100}$, $\frac{13}{25}$, $\frac{27}{50}$, $\frac{11}{20}$ b) $\sqrt{26}$, 5.1, $\frac{41}{8}$, $5\frac{1}{5}$

6 a) 60 b) 45 c) 40

7 a) 5.12 b) 4.19 c) 1.4 d) 24.48
   e) 1.702 f) 6.5 g) 72.5 h) 30
   i) 45 j) 1.05 k) 24 000 l) 84.1
   m) $0.28\dot{3}$ n) 0.06 o) 0.156 p) 9070

8 a) 31.6 b) 45 c) £490.93

9 a) £30 b) 12% c) £309.60 d) £332

10 a) Philip $63.\dot{3}$% non-smokers;
   Samit $67.\dot{2}\dot{7}$% non-smokers.

Page 7: Multiplying fractions

1 a) $\frac{1}{6}$ b) $\frac{3}{16}$ c) $\frac{3}{20}$ d) $\frac{5}{8}$

   e) $\frac{1}{4}$ f) $\frac{3}{5}$ g) $\frac{15}{64}$ h) $7\frac{1}{2}$

2 a) $3\frac{1}{2}$ b) $4\frac{1}{2}$ c) $2\frac{2}{3}$ d) $1\frac{3}{5}$

   e) $12\frac{1}{2}$ f) $9\frac{1}{3}$ g) $3\frac{3}{4}$ h) $7\frac{1}{2}$

3 a) $3\frac{1}{4}$ b) $3\frac{3}{8}$ c) $\frac{7}{8}$ d) $1\frac{3}{4}$

   e) $1\frac{3}{4}$ f) 4 g) $3\frac{3}{4}$ h) $7\frac{7}{8}$

   i) $5\frac{1}{2}$ j) 20 k) $4\frac{13}{16}$ l) 12

4 $27\frac{1}{2}$

5 a) (i) 88 cm (ii) 176 cm
   b) It has doubled (× 2)
   c) (i) 616 cm^2 (ii) 2464 cm^2
   d) It has quadrupled (× 4)

6 $36\frac{1}{4}$ lbs

Page 9: Dividing fractions

1 a) $1\frac{1}{4}$ b) $\frac{1}{10}$ c) $\frac{2}{5}$ d) $\frac{1}{9}$

   e) $\frac{1}{2}$ f) $\frac{3}{4}$ g) $\frac{5}{16}$ h) $\frac{1}{4}$

2 a) 12 b) 6 c) 16 d) 30

   e) $\frac{7}{8}$ f) $1\frac{4}{5}$ g) 10 h) $1\frac{3}{4}$

   i) $\frac{3}{4}$ j) 7 k) $2\frac{1}{2}$ l) $3\frac{3}{5}$

3 a) 10 b) 20

4 40

5 28

6 a) 39 b) 26 c) 18

Page 11: Percentage problems

1 a) £4000 b) £3822.44 c) 20% d) 18.8%

2 a) 200 b) Disco c) 15% d) $\frac{1}{4}$

3 a) 48 feet by 36 feet b) 1728 square feet
   c) 44% d) £38

4 a) £18 b) £17.79 c) £150 d) 10%

Page 13: Further percentage problems

1 a) £160 b) £127.66.44 c) £59.57

2 a) £12 500 b) £13 520

3 a) West
   b) NW 14182, NE 14947, SW 14554, SE 14785
   c) + 2.3%

4 a) £280 000 b) £189 000 c) £378 000, £408 240

Page 15: Repeated changes

1 a) £288 c) £558.90 b) £384.75

2 a) 3720 b) 3721

3 a) 420 b) 560

4 a) £3200 b) £2560 c) 36%

5 a) £1575 b) £1638 c) unchanged

Chapter 2: Formulae and equations

Pages 18–19: Revision exercise

1 a) 12 b) 15 c) 18 d) 10 e) 0
   f) 20 g) 0 h) 100 i) 0 j) 28

2 a) −10 b) −2 c) −17 d) −4x e) m f) 0

3 a) $3a + 6b$ b) $12 − 6x$ c) $15c$ d) $3n^4$

4 a) −15 b) 4 c) −3 d) −3 e) 4
   f) 13 g) −6y h) 2m

5 a) $x = 81$ b) $x = 7$ c) $y = 69$ d) $x = 17.4$
   e) $x = 9$ f) $x = −3\frac{1}{2}$

6 a) $2n - 6$ b) $7a - 7b + 7c$
   c) $20a + 24$ d) $12y - 6z$

7 a) $5n - 1$ b) 5

8 a) $2x + 17$ b) $17 + y$ c) $1 + 4n$ d) $13 - 3a$

9 a) $y = x^2$ because y increases faster than x.

   b) $y = \dfrac{1}{x}$ because y gets smaller as x gets bigger.

   c) $y = x$ because x and y are always equal.

Page 21: Substituting into a formula

1 a) (i) 88   (ii) 100   (iii) 106
   b) (i) 48   (ii) 54

2 a) 10   b) 50   c) 64

3 a) 1 m^3 b) $1\frac{9}{16} \text{ m}^3 = 1.56 \text{ m}^3$

4 80 m

5 a) 6 m

6 a) 5, moving upwards
   b) 3, moving upwards
   c) 0, at the top
   d) –5, moving downwards

Page 23: Working with unknowns

1 a) $4n + 8$ b) $5m - 10$ c) $28 + 14x$
   d) $16 - 24y$ e) $11 - 3x$ f) $10n + 10$
   g) $6x$ h) $3x$ i) $25x - 6$
   j) $8 - 2n$ k) $7 - 3a$ l) $6 - 2x$

2 a) $n, n - 1, n + 3, 3$
   b) $n, n + 2, 2n + 4, 2n + 2, n + 1, 1$
   c) $n, 10n, 10n + 2, 30n + 6, 30n, 30$
   d) $n, n - 1, 5n - 5, 5n, 5$

3 a) divide answer by 10
   b) $n, n + 10, 10n + 100, 10n$

4 a) $n, n - 1, 4n - 4, 4n + 4, n + 1$, *subtract 1*
   b) $n, n + 3, 3n + 9, 3n + 6, n + 2$, *subtract 2*
   c) $n, n - 1, 10n - 10, 10n - 20, n - 2$, *add 2*

Page 25: Using equations to solve problems

1 a) $x = 10$ b) $x = 6$ c) $x = 10$ d) $x = 3$
   e) $x = 3$ f) $x = 4$ g) $x = 3$ h) $x = 0$
   i) $x = 1$

2 a) (i) $12x + 16 = 100$ (ii) $x = 7$
   b) (i) $3w + 6 = 72$ (ii) $w = 22$
   c) (i) $2(3w + w) = 600$ (ii) $w = 75$
   d) (i) $4A + 60 + A = 180$ (ii) $A = 24$
   e) (i) $3y = y + 24$ (ii) $h = 12$

3 a) A-serve: £15
     Beeline: £$(5 + 2x)$
     Comic: £$(9 + 1.5x)$
     When $x = 1$, Beeline is cheapest
     When $x = 10$, A-serve is cheapest
   b) $x = 5$ c) $x = 8$ d) $x = 4$ e) A-serve is cheapest for a total of more than 10 hours otherwise use Beeline.

Page 27: Using graphs to solve equations

1 a) 5.6
   b) 1.66
   c) 5.62

2 a)

x	−2	−1	0	1	2	3	4
x^3	−8	−1	0	1	8	27	64
$-3x^2$	−12	−3	0	−3	−12	−27	−48
$-x$	+2	+1	0	−1	−2	−3	−4
$+3$	+3	+3	+3	+3	+3	+3	+3
y	−15	0	+3	0	−3	0	15

   b) Ask your teacher to check your graph.
   c) (i) −1, 1, 3   (ii) 3.6 or 3.7
   d) 3.65

3 a)

x	1	2	3	4
y	5	−2	$-\frac{1}{3}$	5

   b) Ask your teacher to check your graph.
   c) 1.4, 3.1
   d) 1.43, 3.08

Page 29: Changing the subject of a formula

1 a) $x = y - 4$ b) $x = y - 20$ c) $x = y - a$
   d) $x = y - 3$ e) $x = y - 13$ f) $x = y - c$
   g) $x = y + 5$ h) $x = y + 11$ i) $x = y + b$
   j) $x = 6 - y$ k) $x = 1 - y$ l) $x = d - y$

2 a) $x = \frac{1}{2}y$ b) $x = 10y$ c) $x = \frac{y}{a}$
   d) $x = 4y$ e) $x = 10y$ f) $x = by$
   g) $x = \frac{4}{3}y$ h) $x = \frac{3}{5}y$ i) $x = \frac{b}{a}y$
   j) $x = \frac{5}{4}y$ k) $x = \frac{2}{11}y$ l) $x = \frac{b}{a}y$

3 a) $t = \frac{x + 3}{2}$ b) $t = \frac{y - 4}{3}$ c) $t = \frac{p - 6}{2}$
   d) $t = 4 - c$ e) $t = \frac{6 - z}{2}$ f) $t = \frac{s - a}{2}$
   g) $t = \frac{x + c}{5}$ h) $t = \frac{n + 3x}{7}$

4 a) $u = v - at$ b) $l = \frac{p - 2b}{2}$
   c) $x = \frac{V + 9y}{4}$ d) $t = \frac{v - u}{a}$

5 a) $x = \frac{p - 2y}{2}$ or $\frac{p}{2} - y$ or $\frac{V}{12} - r$
   b) $x = \frac{V - 12r}{12}$
   c) $x = \frac{8 - s}{4}$ d) $x = \frac{4a - y}{4}$ or $a - \frac{y}{4}$

6 a) $l = \frac{A}{b}$ b) $h = \frac{V}{lb}$ c) $R = \frac{V}{I}$
   d) $d = \frac{c}{\pi}$ e) $r = \frac{c}{2\pi}$ f) $P = \frac{100I}{r}$
   g) $T = \frac{100I}{PR}$ h) $R = \frac{100I}{PT}$

Chapter 3: Triangles and polygons

Page 33: Revision exercise

1 Ask your teacher to check your tessellations.

2 $a = 82°$ $b = 96°$ $c = 62°$ $d = 30°$
   $e = 103°$ $f = 77°$ $g = 103°$ $h = 111°$
   $i = 69°$ $j = 111°$ $k = 111°$ $l = 69°$
   $m = 58°$ $n = 62°$ $p = 67°$ $q = 113°$
   $r = 74°$ $s = 106°$ $t = 74°$ $u = 89°$
   $v = 89°$ $w = 47°$

3 900°, 1260°

4 a) Interior angle = 120°, exterior angle = 60°
   b) Interior angle = 144°, exterior angle = 36°

Page 35: More about angles in polygons

1 a) 10   b) 12   c) 8

2 a) 60°   b) 3

3 a) 140°   b) No

4 a) 90°   b) Square

5 a) (i) $x = 110°$, $y = 35°$, $z = 55°$
     (ii) ACB = 90°
   c) The angle ACB is always 90°.

6 $a = 36°$, $b = 99°$

Page 37: Pythagoras' Rule

1 a) 8.06 cm   b) 8.49 cm   c) 13.60 cm   d) 13.45 cm
   e) 8.16 cm   f) 9.17 cm

2 192 m

3 28.6 km

4 a) 3 units   b) 2 units   c) 3.61 units

5 a) 5.39 units   b) 4.24 units
   c) 5.10 units   d) 4.47 units

Page 39: Finding one of the shorter sides

1 a) 6.24 cm   b) 8.94 cm   c) 4.47 cm   d) 8.02 cm
   e) 4.08 cm   f) 7.07 cm

2 2.44 m

3 a) 5.66 cm   b) 11.3 cm^2

4 a) 3 cm   b) 6 cm^2 c) 2.4 cm
   d) AN = 3.2 cm, CN = 1.8 cm

Chapter 4: Grouped data

Page 42: Revision exercise

1 a) discrete   b) continuous   c) discrete
   d) continuous   e) continuous

2 a) 75   b) 60
   c) Ask your teacher to check your diagrams.

3 a) 24   b) 131   c) mode 7   d) range 6
   e) mean 5.46

4 a) Ask your teacher to check your tally chart.
   b)

Score	0–9	10–19	20–29	30–39	40–49	50–59	60–69
Frequency	1	9	8	3	5	4	6

   c) 10–19   d) Yes   e) 59
   f) A 195, B 178, C 192, D 183, E 202, F 294.
     No – team F is much better than the others.
     The rest are reasonably evenly matched.

Page 45: Grouping continuous date

1 a)

Mileage (thousands)	$0 \leq m < 10$	$10 \leq m < 20$	$20 \leq m < 30$	$30 \leq m < 40$	$40 \leq m < 50$
Frequency	1	2	5	2	2

   b) Ask your teacher to check your histogram.
   c) (i) Total price: A £118,000, B £123,000.
       B is best.
     (ii) Sell 2 highest mileage to A and rest to B.
       £125,000

2 a)

Reading	$70 \leq m < 71$	$71 \leq m < 72$	$72 \leq m < 73$	$73 \leq m < 74$	$74 \leq m < 75$
Frequency	0	1	4	5	10

Reading	$75 \leq m < 76$	$76 \leq m < 77$	$77 \leq m < 78$
Frequency	4	4	2

   b) Ask your teacher to check your histogram.
   c) less than 72 or more than 78, i.e. only 1 reading

Page 47: Grouping rounded data

1 a) 5.5 and 10.5   b) 8
   c) just under 20.5 minutes   d) 0.5 mins
   e) Ask your teacher to check your histogram.

2 a) 70.5 and 140.5   b) 105.5
   c) just under 280.5 g
   d) Ask your teacher to check your histogram.

3 a)

Age in years	16–20	21–25	26–30	31–35	36–40	41–45	51–55	66–70
Frequency	2	11	6	5	2	2	1	1

   b) Ask your teacher to check your histogram.
   c) add 1 to each of the labels on the x axis

4 a) 15 sq units (each sq unit represents 1 bus)
   b) 15 sq units. The area of the histogram is the
     same as the area under the frequency polygon.

Page 49: Mean, median and mode of grouped data

1 a) 6 – 10 kg   b) 8 kg   c) 430 kg   d) 8.6 kg

2 a) £51 000 – £60 000   b) £105 500

   c) $\frac{£7036500}{143} = £49206$

3 a) 90 – 94 mins   b) 92.25 mins

   c) 92.5 mins (approx 25 mins added to total)

   d) modal class still 90 – 94 mins

Page 51: Quartiles

1 a) Ask your teacher to check your cumulative frequency chart.

   b) median 9 days, UQ 14 days, LQ 5.5 or 6 days, IQ range 8.5 or 8 days

   c) 105   d) 11

2 a)

Number of laps completed	2	4	6	8	10	12	14
Number of children still swimming	50	44	34	16	8	3	0
Number stopping	0	6	16	34	42	47	50

   b, c) Ask your teacher to check your graphs.

   c) standard cumulative frequency curve

   d) Axis of symmetry is $y = 25$

Page 53: Making comparisons

1 a) Shop A, 6–10. Shop B, 16–20

   b) Ask your teacher to check your frequency polygons.

   c) Fewer items are bought in shop A than in shop B (lower modal class) but the range is the same.

   d) A is probably a smaller shop because most people just buy a few items. B is probably a supermarket.

2 a) Ask your teacher to check your cumulative frequency chart.

   b) Northbound: median 3.25 mins, IQ range 4 mins 40 secs – 2 mins = 2 mins 40 secs
Southbound: median 7 mins, IQ range 9 mins – 5 mins = 4 mins

   c) Southbound traffic has longer delays which could be helped by setting traffic lights with longer at green for Southbound traffic.

   d) Yes. If this is morning rush hour then the traffic pattern would be reversed in the evening rush hour.

Chapter 5: Simultaneous equations

Page 59: Using simultaneous equations

1 a) $x = 7$ b) $14 + y = 15$ so $y = 1$ c) $7 + 1 = 8$

2 a) 4, 9   b) 10, 1   c) 6, –1   d) 2, 2
   e) 5, 3   f) 6, 1   g) 1, 5   h) 100, 200
   i) –2, 3

3 a) 7, 3   b) 3, $\frac{1}{3}$ c) 9, 11   d) 1, 0

   e) 2, –1   f) 5, $\frac{1}{2}$

4 White costs £2, blue £2.50

5 Oranges cost 40p, apples cost 30p

Page 61: More simultaneous equations

1 a) 10, 2   b) 18, 3   c) 8, 5

   d) 9, 5   e) 7, –1   f) $11\frac{1}{2}, 1\frac{1}{2}$

2 a) $20x - 4y = 208$ b) $23x = 230$ c) 10, –2

3 a) 20, 11   b) $\frac{1}{2}, 1$ c) 10, 5   d) 5, 2   e) 5, 1

   f) $1\frac{1}{2}, 4$ g) $8, 3\frac{1}{2}$ h) 10, 2   i) 50, 13

4 Jam doughnuts cost 18p, ring doughnuts 12p.
She could buy 11 (with 2p change).

5 Carl is 34, his father 66 years old.

Page 63: Multiplying both equations

1 a) $6x + 10y = 580$ b) $25x - 10y = 350$
   c) $31x = 930$ d) 30, 40

2 a) 9, 2   b) 8, 0   c) 10, 2   d) 5, –1   e) 0, 5
   f) $\frac{1}{2}, 1$ g) 9, 7   h) 10, 20

3 5 trays of barfi, 3 of halwa

4 Basic rate is £3.50, rate after 11 p.m. is £6 per hour.

5 Carnations cost 50p, roses 90p.

Page 65: Other methods of solution

1 a) 4, 6   b) 6, 10   c) 4, 3   d) 5, 1
   e) 6, –5   f) 1, 2

2 a) $x + 2y = 12$ b) $x + y = 8$ c) 4, 4

3 5 in a packet, 20 in a box

4 a) 35, 71   b) 2, 5   c) $2\frac{1}{2}, \frac{1}{2}$ d) –1, 5
   e) 1, –1   f) 6, 1

Chapter 6: Trigonometry

Page 69: Introduction to trigonometry

1

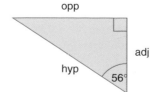

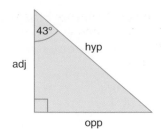

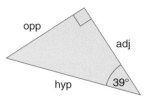

Your answers to questions 2 and 3 may be slightly different (up to about 0.05 either way) from those given. This is because it is not possible to measure accurately.

2 b) 0.84   c) 0.64   d) 0.77
3 b) 1.33   b) 0.80   d) 0.60

Page 71: Using tangent (tan)

1 a) 0.466   b) 3.271   c) 1   d) 0.754
   e) 1.235   f) 7.115
2 a) 3.63 cm b) 4.43 cm c) 5.60 cm d) 3.78 cm
   e) 9.20 cm f) 2.98 cm
3 33.7 m

Page 73: Finding the adjacent side using tan

1 $a = 3.90$ cm $b = 9.40$ cm $c = 5.78$ cm
2 $d = 60.0°$ $e = 66.9°$ $f = 47.3°$
3 $p = 4.40$ cm $q = 46.3°$ $r = 4.93$ cm
   $s = 28.7°$ $t = 3.56$ cm $u = 3.08$ cm

Page 75: Using sine (sin)

1 $a = 4.46$ cm $b = 8.99$ cm $c = 6.19$ cm $d = 8.04$ cm
   $e = 5.00$ cm $f = 7.12$ cm
2 $p = 50.2°$ $q = 37.3°$ $r = 37.6°$
3 a) 7.73 m b) 48.6°

Page 77: Using cosine (cos)

1 $a = 4.82$ cm $b = 8.40$ cm $c = 6.87$ cm $d = 5.35$ cm
   $e = 8.65$ cm $f = 6.48$ cm
2 $x = 57.6°$ $y = 33.3°$ $z = 59.0°$
3 2.008 km

Page 79: Using sin, cos and tan

1 $a = 6.86$ cm $b = 4.17$ cm $c = 9.85$ cm $d = 5.70$ cm
   $e = 8.49$ cm $f = 3.96$ cm $g = 3.87$ cm $h = 8.48$ cm
   $i = 9.12$ cm
2 $p = 53.6°$ $q = 37.3°$ $r = 39.1°$ $s = 51.5°$
   $t = 48.7°$ $u = 60.3°$

Page 81: Using trigonometry

1 a) 127 km south, 272 km west
   b) 409 km north, 368 km west
2 1067 m
3 a) 932 m   b) 12.5°
4 a) 2.12 m   b) 1.5 m
5 6.9 m
6 a) 84.5 km south, 181.3 km east
   b) 96.4 km south, 114.9 km west
   c) 180.9 km south, 66.4 km east
   d) 340°

Chapter 7: Inequalities

Page 85: Using inequalities

1 a) $x > 3$ b) $x \geq 0$ c) $x < 5$ d) $x \leq -2$
2 a) x is less than 8   b) p is greater than 100
   c) q is greater than or equal to 100
   d) y is less than 17
   e) x is less than or equal to 20
   f) b is greater than or equal to -3
3 a) $2 < 9$ b) $13 > 3$ c) $-3 > -13$ d) $13 > -3$
   e) $3.8 > 3.3$ f) $0.5 < 0.625$
4 a) $s \leq 30$ b) $f \geq 79$ c) $g \geq 20$ d) $p \leq 5$
   e) $c < 250$ f) $n \geq 50$ g) $w \leq 2.5$ h) $d \geq 500$
5 a) $9 > 2$ b) $3 < 13$ c) $13 > -3$ d) $-3 > -13$
   e) $3.3 < 3.8$ f) $0.625 > 0.5$

Page 87: Number lines

1 a) 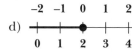   b)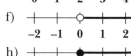

   c)   d)

   e)   f)

   g) 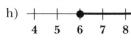   h)

   i)

2 a) $w \leq 60$ b)

3 a) 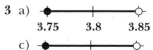   b)

   c) 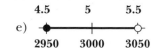   d)

   e) 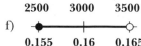   f)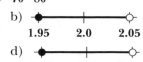

4 a)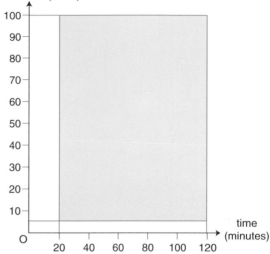

(number line 2 to 8, filled dots at 3 and 7)

b) (number line −3 to 6, filled dots at −3 and 5)

c) (number line −5 to 1, filled dot at −4, open circle at 0)

d) (number line 1.65 to 1.75, filled dot at 1.65, open circle at 1.75)   **e)** (number line −2 to 1, open circle at −1, filled dot at 0)

f) (number line −7 to −1, open circle at −6, open circle at −3)

g) (number line −1 to 4, filled dot at 2)

h) (number line 0 to 7, filled dot at 2)

5 $x < 10$,   1, 2, 3, 4, 5, 6, 7, 8, 9

(number line 0 to 10 with crosses at 1–9)

6 a)

x	−4	−3	−2	−1	0	1	2	3	4
x^2	16	9	4	1	0	1	4	9	16

b) (i) (number line −5 to 5, filled dots at −4 and 4)

(ii) (number line −4 to 4, filled dots at −3 and 3)

(iii) (number line −10 to 10, open circles at −5 and 5)   **(iv)** (number line −2 to 2, open circles at −1 and 1)

c) $x^2 > 4$ **d)** $x^2 \leq 1$

Page 89: Solving inequalities

1 a) $x < 6$ **b)** $x \leq 5$ **c)** $x \geq 8$ **d)** $x \geq 4$ **e)** $x < 3$
f) $x > 6$ **g)** $x \leq 3.6$ **h)** $x \leq 8$ **i)** $x > 2$ **j)** $x \leq 2$
k) $x \geq 3$ **l)** $x \leq -3$

2 a) 2, 3, 5, 7, 11, 13, 17, 19
b) 25, 36   **c)** 4, 6   **d)** 6, 9

3 a) $5x - 200$ **b)** $5x - 200 > x; \ x > 50$

4 $w + 52 > 14 \, w, \ w < 4$

5 a) $x \geq 11$ **b)** $x \geq 2$ **c)** $x > 7$ **d)** $x < 6$

e) $1 \leq x \leq 8$ **f)** $10 \geq x > 3$ **g)** $6\frac{1}{2} < x < 9\frac{1}{2}$

h) $2 \leq x \leq 20$ **i)** $2 < x \leq 11$ **f)** $x > 11$
k) $x \geq 16$ **l)** $x > 1$

Page 91: Inequalities and graphs

1 a) $-1 \leq x \leq 2, \ 0 \leq y \leq 2$ **b)** $x > 2, \ y > 1$
c) $0 \leq x \leq 3, \ 0 \leq y \leq 1$ **d)** $3 < x < 10, \ 5 \leq y \leq 10$
e) $x \geq 4, \ y \geq 3$ **f)** $1 \leq x \leq 4, \ y > -1$

2 Ask your teacher to check your graphs.
3 a) $20 \leq t \leq 120$, t is time in minutes
    $5 \leq d \leq 100$

b) distance (miles)

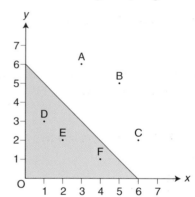

Page 93: Regions bounded by sloping lines

1 a), b) + d)

(graph with points A, B, C, D, E, F and shaded triangular region bounded by line from (0,6) to (6,0))

c)

point	$x + y$
A	9
B	10
C	8
D	4
E	4
F	5

2 a) ,b) + d)

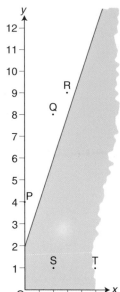

c)
point	2x + 2
P	2
Q	6
R	8
S	6
T	12

3 a), b) + c)

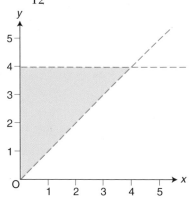

d) Points on the lines are not included.

4 a) $2x + 2y$

b) The perimeter can't be longer than the 500 cm strip.

c) $x > 80$

d) Ask your teacher to check your graph.

5 a)

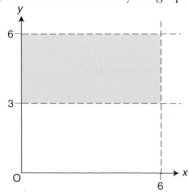

b)

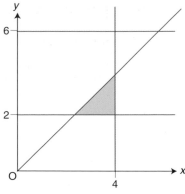

c)

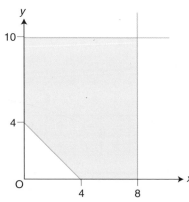

d)

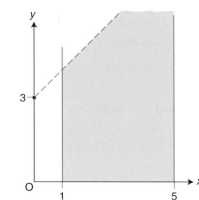

Page 95: Solution sets

1 a), c) + d) Ask your teacher to check your graph.

b) At $(1, 2)$ $x + 3y = 7$

$(2, 4)$ $x + 3y = 12$

2 a) $2w + 4s \geq 10$ or $w + 2s \geq 5$

b) $w \leq 5$

c) $s \leq 2$

d) Ask your teacher to check your graph.

3 a) $x + y \leq 21$ b) $4x + 7y \geq 56$

Ask your teacher to check your graph.

c), d) Ask your teacher to check your graph.

e) $(10\frac{1}{2}, 10\frac{1}{2})$ f) £114

Chapter 8: Indices and standard form

Pages 98–99: Revision exercise

1 a) 8   b) 36   c) 81   d) 64   e) 243
   f) 256   g) 121   h) 3.375

2 a) 81   b) 9   c) 125   d) 5   e) 8000
   f) 7   g) 10   h) 160 000

3 a) 64   b) 512

4 a) 10   b) 14 by 14   c) 4

5 a) 520   b) 8.3   c) 0.69   d) 2300   e) 0.47
   f) 64   g) 7   h) 5.28   i) 9345   j) 8
   k) 0.912   l) 573 000   m) 0.075   n) 393.71
   o) 140.65   p) 10 560

6 a) 280 000 000 000   b) 57 200 000 000 000

Pages 101: Rules of indices

1 a) $\frac{1}{16}$ b) $\frac{1}{1000}$ c) $\frac{1}{25}$ d) $\frac{1}{8}$ e) $\frac{1}{27}$ f) $\frac{1}{36}$
   g) $\frac{1}{100}$ h) $\frac{1}{81}$ i) $\frac{1}{4}$ j) $\frac{1}{16}$ k) $\frac{1}{216}$
   l) $\frac{1}{10\,000}$

2 a) 49   b) $\frac{1}{9}$ c) $\frac{1}{10}$ d) 64   e) $\frac{1}{81}$ f) 1
   g) 32   h) $\frac{1}{125}$ i) 1000 000   j) 9   k) $\frac{1}{5}$
   l) 1   m) 216   n) $\frac{1}{64}$ o) 4   p) 625

3 a) 5^6 b) 2^{11} c) 6^4 d) 10^3 e) 2^7 f) 10^6
   g) 3^8 h) 4^2 i) 10^4 j) 5^{-2} k) 3^3 l) 2
   m) 4^2 n) 3^{-2} o) 2^0 p) 10^3

Page 103: Standard form

1 a) 600   b) 30 000   c) 0.007   d) 0.000 04
   e) 4 500 000   f) 0.0054   g) 9400   h) 0.000 875
   i) 0.016   j) 2 750 000   k) 0.000 083
   l) 10 500   m) 7300   n) 0.000 000 008
   o) 0.4   p) 82 500 000 000

2 a) 4×10^3 b) 8×10^5 c) 3×10^{-3}
   d) 9×10^{-4} e) 2.6×10^4 f) 2.5×10^{-2}
   g) 7.5×10^6 h) 3.7×10^{-5} i) 8.1×10^2
   j) 5.43×10^{-3} k) 9.3×10^{-1} l) 6.4×10^4
   m) 1.6×10^{-2} n) 1.47×10^8 o) 5.07×10^{-1}
   p) 9.04×10^3

3 a) 0.005   b) 4 600 000 000 000
   c) 942 000 000   d) 0.000 0075

4 Pluto (smallest), Mercury, Mars, Venus, Earth,
Neptune, Uranus, Saturn, Jupiter (largest)

Page 105: Calculations using standard form

1 a) 8.4×10^4 b) 6.8×10^6 c) 1.5×10^{12}
   d) 1.6×10^7 e) 1.5×10^9 f) 7.02×10^{-2}
   g) 1.44×10^{-17} h) 1.6×10^{15}

2 Mercury 7.86×10^{22} kg
   Venus 4.88×10^{24} kg
   Mars 2.05×10^{23} kg
   Jupiter 2.04×10^{27} kg

3 1.8×10^{-16} J

4 a) Europe   b) 9 million   c) 30 million km^2

5 a) 2.06×10^{19} m^3 b) 3592 kg/m^3

Chapter 9: Manipulating expressions

Page 109: Like terms

1 a) Yes   b) Yes   c) No   d) No   e) No
   f) Yes

2 a) $2x^2 + 3x^2 = 5x^2$, $4x + 7x = 11x$
   b) $y^2 + 2y^2 - y^2 = 2y^2$, $3y + y = 4y$
   c) $3u^2 + 6u^2 = 9u^2$, $4u - 2u + u - 2u = u$
   d) $3p + 6p + 6p = 15p$, $-3p^2 + 5p^2 = 2p^2$, $3 + 2 - 6 = -1$

3 a) $8x + 3y$ b) $10a + 10b$ c) $3p + 4q$
   d) $10s + 9t$ e) $5l + 13m$ f) $5h$
   g) $4x + 3$ h) $2x - 2y + 3$ i) $6a - 6c$
   j) $8p + 11$

4 a) $x^2 + 2x + 1$ b) $x^2 - 2x - 3$ c) $y^2 - 3y + 2$
   d) $2y^2 - 2y + 7$ e) $8a^2 - a$ f) $7 - 5x + x^2$
   g) $-2d$ h) $10x^2 - x + 2$ i) $12x - 5x^2$
   j) $t^2 + 9$

5 a) $3m + 2m^2$ b) $3k + 2k^2$ c) $20x + 2x^2$
   d) $4y$ e) $x^2 - 2x - 8$ f) $a^2 + 4a + 4$
   g) $h^2 - 4h + 5$ h) $h^2 - 9h + 18$ i) $x^2 - 2x^3$

Page 111: Factorising

1 a) 4   b) 3   c) a d) 5, b, $5b$

2 a) $12 = 3 \times 4$ $3c = 3 \times c$
   b) $16 = 8 \times 2$ $8y = 8 \times y$
   c) $n = n \times 1$ $7n^2 = n \times 7n$
   d) $10x = 5x \times 2$ $5x^2 = 5x \times x$
   e) $14y = 7y \times 2$ $7y^2 = 7y \times y$
   f) $4x^2 = 2x \times 2x$ $6x = 2x \times 3$

3 a) $4(t + 2)$ b) $3(2 - m)$ c) $2(1 + 9b)$
   d) $5(x + 2)$ e) $3(3z - 11)$ f) $5(x - 1)$
   g) $2(a + 3b + 2c)$ h) $3(x - y + 3z)$ i) $2(a - 11b + 3c)$
   j) $2(4p + 3p - 2r)$ k) $7(2l - m - 7n)$
   l) $8(2a + 3b - 4c)$

4 a) $x(2 + x)$ b) $y(3 - 2y)$ c) $x(5x - 4)$
   d) $y(10y + 7)$ e) $3(x^2 + 4x + 2)$ f) $7(3 + x - 2x^2)$
   g) $4(2g^2 - 4g - 1)$ h) $5(3 + x + 4x^2)$
   i) $6y(y - 2x)$ j) $y^2(3x - 11)$ k) $4t(s + 2)$
   l) $3a(b - 2c + 3d)$

5 a) $4(2x + 9y)$ b) $11(x + 3)$ c) $5(3p + 4q)$
   d) $5(2x + y)$ e) $4(5a + 4c)$ f) $5(l + n)$
   g) $6(x + 3y)$ h) $7(p + 2q)$ i) $2(x - 2y)$
   j) $2(r + s)$ k) $x^2 + 9$ l) $x(x - 8)$

Page 113: Expanding two brackets

1 a) $6a$ b) $6c^2$ c) $20y^2$
d) $-6x$ e) $-12x$ f) $15x$

2 a) $x^2 + 4x + 3$ b) $y^2 + 7y + 10$ c) $12 + 7x + x^2$
d) $30 + 11y + y^2$ e) $x^2 + x - 2$ f) $y^2 + y - 6$
g) $x^2 - 4x - 12$ h) $y^2 - 4y - 5$ i) $x^2 - 9x + 14$
j) $y^2 - 7y + 12$ k) $x^2 - 8x + 15$ l) $y^2 - 11y + 30$

3 a) $400 + 20 + 20 + 1 = 441$
b) $900 + 30 + 30 + 1 = 961$
c) $x^2 + 2x + 1$ d) 1681

4 a) $a^2 + 6a + 9$ b) $x^2 + 10x + 25$ c) $a^2 - 6a + 9$
d) $x^2 - 10x + 25$ e) $4y^2 + 4y + 1$ f) $9x^2 + 12x + 4$

5 a) $6x^2 + 19x + 10$ b) $6x^2 - 19x + 10$
c) $6x^2 + 11x - 10$ d) $6x^2 - 11x - 10$

6 a) $xy + x + y + 1$ b) $ad + 2a + 3d + 6$
c) $xy - x - y + 1$ d) $ck - 10c + 4k - 40$
e) $ax + 4a - 3x - 12$ f) $xy - x + 10y - 10$

7 a) $(x+1)(x+2)$ b) $x^2, 2x, x, 2$
c) $x^2 + 2x + x + 2 = x^2 + 3x + 2$ d) C and B

Page 115: Squares

1 c) 4 d) $4x^2$

2 a) $9x^2$ b) $25y^2$ c) $9x^2$
d) $25y^2$ e) $16a^2$ f) $100u^2$

3 a) $x^2 + 8x + 16$ b) $y^2 + 6y + 9$ c) $c^2 - 6c + 9$
d) $n^2 - 10n + 25$ e) $4x^2 + 20x + 25$
f) $9 + 12t + 4t^2$ g) $4y^2 - 12y + 9$
h) $25d^2 - 10d + 1$ i) $x^2 - 16$ j) $y^2 - 9$
k) $4x^2 - 25$ l) $9 - 4t^2$

4 a) $x^2 + 2xy + y^2$ b) $x^2 - 2xy + y^2$ c) $x^2 + 14x + 49$
d) $x^2 - 14x + 49$ e) $4x^2 + 12x + 9$
f) $16n^2 - 24n + 9$ g) $25 + 10z + z^2$
h) $9 - 6x + x^2$ i) $4x^2 + 12xy + 9y^2$
j) $4x^2 - 12xy + 9y^2$ k) $x^2 - y^2$ l) $x^2 - 49$
m) $4x^2 - 1$ n) $16n^2 - 81$ o) $25 - z^2$
p) $9p^2 - q^2$ q) $4x^2 - 9y^2$ r) $100a^2 - 4b^2$

5 a) $(20-1)(20+1)$
b) $20^2 - 1^2 = 399$
c) $(30-1)(30+1) = 900 - 1$
$= 899$

Chapter 10: Probability

Pages 118–119: Revision exercise

1 A 0.5 (exact), B 0 (exact), C 1 (exact), D depends on time of year approx, E very small (approximate), F if marked should be at 1.

2 a) $\frac{1}{3}$ b) $\frac{2}{3}$

3 a) $\frac{100}{125} = \frac{4}{5}$ b) $\frac{20}{125} = \frac{4}{25}$ c) $\frac{4}{125}$ d) $\frac{1}{125}$

4 a) $\frac{4}{30} = \frac{2}{15}$ b) $\frac{12}{30} = \frac{2}{5}$

c) 2 or 3 because the ratio on clear nights is 4 : 14 and the ratio on cloudy nights is probably similar.
d) No

5 a)

		1	2	3	4	5	6
	1	2	3	4	5	6	7
	2	3	4	5	6	7	8
blue die	3	4	5	6	7	8	9
	4	5	6	7	8	9	10
	5	6	7	8	9	10	11
	6	7	8	9	10	11	12

red die

b) (i) $\frac{6}{36} = \frac{1}{6}$ (ii) $\frac{2}{36} = \frac{1}{18}$ (iii) $\frac{2}{36} = \frac{1}{18}$
(iv) $\frac{3}{36} = \frac{1}{12}$ (v) $\frac{6}{36} = \frac{1}{6}$

Page 121: Two outcomes: 'either, or'

1 a) $\frac{8}{52} = \frac{2}{13}$ b) $\frac{16}{52} = \frac{4}{13}$

2 a) $\frac{5}{20} = \frac{1}{4}$ b) $\frac{15}{20} = \frac{3}{4}$ c) $\frac{13}{20}$ d) $\frac{7}{20}$

3 a) $\frac{3}{65}$ b) $\frac{29}{65}$ c) $\frac{18}{65}$

4 a) $\frac{6}{36} = \frac{1}{6}$ b) $\frac{15}{36} = \frac{5}{12}$ c) $\frac{9}{36} = \frac{1}{4}$ d) $\frac{15}{36} = \frac{5}{12}$

Page 123: Two outcomes: 'first, then'

1 a) $\frac{1}{4}$ or 0.25 b) $\frac{1}{2}$ or 0.5

2 a) 0.1 b) 0.01 c) 0.009 d) 0.729

3 a) $\frac{1}{8}$ b) $\frac{1}{8}$ c) $\frac{1}{8}$ d) $\frac{3}{8}$ e) $\frac{1}{8}$

4 a) $\frac{1}{4}$ or 0.25 b) $\frac{1}{5}$ or 0.2 c) $\frac{1}{20}$ or 0.05
d) $\frac{1}{60}$ e) $\frac{3}{10}$

Page 125: Probability trees

1 a) 0.18 b) 0.28 c) 0.12 d) 0.42

2 a) (i) 10 (ii) 30
b) Smartie colour   Fred's guess

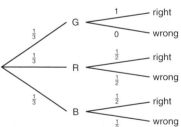

c) P(right) $= \frac{2}{3}$ d) Yes

Chapter 11: Locus

Page 129: Simple loci

1 a)

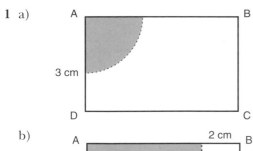

b)

c)

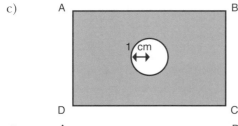

d)

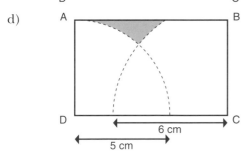

e)

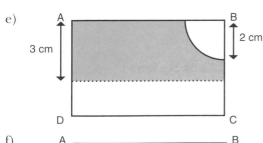

f)

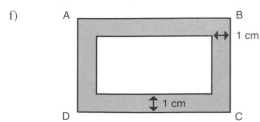

2 Ask your teacher to check your diagram.
3 Ask your teacher to check your diagram.
4 Ask your teacher to check your diagram.
5 Ask your teacher to check your diagram.

Page 131: A point equidistant from two fixed points

2 c) It is the centre of the circle.
3 Ask your teacher to check your diagram.
4 Ask your teacher to check your diagram.

Page 133: A point equidistant from two lines

2 b) It is the same distance from all three sides.
It is also the centre of a circle which just
touches all three sides of the triangle.
3 a) b), c) d) Ask your teacher to check your diagrams.
4 Ask your teacher to check your diagram.

Chapter 12: Ratio and proportion

Pages 136–137: Revision exercise

1 a) 1800   b) $\frac{9}{10}$ c) 10%   d) 7.5 l

2 a) 2 : 1   b) 3 : 4   c) 3 : 2   d) 1 : 3   e) 2 : 5
   f) 2 : 3   g) 5 : 2   h) 8 : 3   i) 3 : 4 : 5
   j) 2 : 3 : 4   k) 2 : 4 : 5   l) 4 : 5 : 9

3 a) 1 : 8   b) 3 : 2   c) 3 : 8   d) 4 : 1   e) 1 : 5
   f) 3 : 20 g) 3 : 4   h) 1 : 20 000

4 a) Bran Flakes 750 g   b) Kitto cat food 2 kg

5 a) £360, £240   b) £120, £420
   c) £500, £750, £1000   d) £1280, £1600, £320

6 a) blackberries 8 lb, sugar 12 lb, water 6 pints
   b) $12\frac{1}{2}$ c) $7\frac{1}{2}$ lbs

7 a) £1200   b) £800   c) 3 : 1
   d) £2500   e) £625   f) $\frac{3}{4}$

Page 139: Unitary method

1 a) £5.45   b) £81.75   c) £201.65   d) 24
2 a) 173.7 g   b) 51.8 cm^3
3 a) rolled oats 525 g; golden sugar 300 g, butter
      225 g, golden syrup 150 g, cranberries 150 g
   b) 30
4 a) 567   b) £28   c) $16.20   d) £12.35
5 54

Page 141: Distance, speed and time

1 a) 100 km   b) 105 km   c) 1980 km   d) 20 km
2 a) 56 km/h   b) 64.8 km/h
   c) 84 km/h
3 a) $2\frac{1}{2}$ h   b) $3\frac{3}{4}$ h   c) 1h 40 min
   d) 2 h 6 m 36 s
4 a) 1240   b) 80 km/h
   c) 64 km/h   d) 35 minutes

Answers

Chapter 13: Quadratics

Page 145: Factorising quadratic expressions

1 a) $1, 5$
  b) $(x + 1)(x + 5)$
2 a) $3, 5$
  b) $(y + 3)(y + 5)$
3 a) $(x + 2)(x + 7)$
  b) $(x + 1)(x + 14)$
  c) $(a + 2)(a + 5)$
  d) $(a + 10)(a + 1)$
  e) $(n + 4)(n + 1)$
  f) $(t + 2)(t + 2)$
  g) $(x + 2)(x + 2)$
  h) $(x + 3)(x + 6)$
  i) $(y + 4)(y + 6)$
4 a) $-1, -5$
  b) $(x - 1)(x - 5)$
5 a) $-3, -5$
  b) $(y - 3)(y - 5)$
6 a) $(x - 1)(x - 2)$
  b) $(x - 3)(x - 1)$
  c) $(x - 5)(x - 1)$
  d) $(x - 11)(x - 1)$
  e) $(x - 7)(x - 2)$
  f) $(x - 2)(x - 4)$
  g) $(p - 3)(p - 6)$
  h) $(a - 4)(a - 11)$
  i) $(x - 44)(x - 1)$
7 a) $(y - 1)^2$
  b) $(a + 2)(a + 11)$
  c) $(x - 3)(x - 7)$
  d) $(p - 2)(p - 8)$
  e) $(t - 2)(t - 6)$
  f) $(y + 3)(y + 4)$
  g) $(a + 1)^2$
  h) $(x + 3)^2$
  i) $(y - 2)^2$
  j) $(t - 5)^2$
  k) $(x - 3)^2$
  l) $(y - 1)(y - 4)$
  m) $(p - 6)^2$
  n) $(x + 7)^2$
  o) $(x - 5)(x - 20)$

Page 147: More quadratic factorisation

1 a) $6, 1$
  b) $(x + 6)(x - 1)$
  c) $(x - 6)(x + 1)$
2 a) $3, 5$
  b) $(y + 5)(y - 3)$
  c) $(y - 5)(y + 3)$
3 a) $(x + 11)(x - 1)$
  b) $(x - 11)(x + 1)$

  c) $(x + 7)(x - 1)$
  d) $(x - 7)(x + 1)$
  e) $(x + 5)(x - 1)$
  f) $(x - 5)(x + 1)$
  g) $(x + 7)(x - 2)$
  h) $(x - 7)(x + 2)$
  i) $(x + 11)(x - 8)$
4 a) $(a + 9)(a - 2)$
  b) $(a - 9)(a + 2)$
  c) $(y + 10)(y - 1)$
  d) $(y + 2)(y - 5)$
  e) $(p - 6)(p + 3)$
  f) $(x + 3)(x - 4)$
  g) $(x + 5)(x - 4)$
  h) $(a - 2)(a + 10)$
  i) $(t + 6)(t - 2)$
5 a) $(x - 2)(x + 2)$
  b) $(y - 5)(y + 5)$
  c) $(z - 1)(z + 1)$
  d) $(n - 4)(n + 4)$
  e) $(t - 7)(t + 7)$
  f) $(p - 10)(p + 10)$
6 a) $(x + 1)(x + 6)$
  b) $(x + 2)(x + 4)$
  c) $(r - 4)(r - 1)$
  d) $(x - 9)(x + 1)$
  e) $(y + 4)(y - 1)$
  f) $(x + 4)(x - 3)$
  g) $(t - 4)(t + 3)$
  h) $(x - 2)(x - 9)$
  i) $(p + 6)(p - 2)$
  j) $(y - 9)(y + 9)$
  k) $(b - 5)(b + 4)$
  l) $(a - 10)(a - 1)$
7 a) $4(x + 4)(x - 3)$
  b) $3(a - 1)(a + 2)$
  c) $3(x - 2)(x + 2)$
  d) $3(x + 1)^2$
  e) $10(x - 10)(x + 10)$
  f) $5(x - 8)(x + 10)$

Page 149: Quadratic equations

1 a) $x = 4$ or 1
  b) $x = 0$ or 4
  c) $x = 4$
  d) $x = 0$ or -4
  e) $y = 0$ or 3
  f) $x = 2$ or 3
  g) $x = 5$ or -3
  h) $t = 0$ or 2
  i) $y = 0$ or -4

2 a) 2, 7
  b) 2, 5
  c) 2, −7
  d) −1, −4
  e) 2, −3
  f) 6, −2
  g) 5, −10
  h) 9, −7
  i) 11, 1
3 a) −5, 4
  b) 2, −10
  c) 1, 4
  d) 4, −1
  e) −2, −9
  f) 4, −3
  g) 2, −8
  h) 2, −2
  i) 5, 6
4 a) (i) $w^2 + 3w - 54 = 0$ (ii) $w = 6$
  b) (i) $8l^2 - 80l - 3000 = 0$ (ii) $l = 25$
  c) (i) $2x^2 + 8x - 90 = 0$ (ii) $x = 5$
5 a)

x	−4	−3	−2	−1	0	1	2	3	4
x^2	20	12	6	2	0	0	2	6	12

  b) −2, 3
  c) −2, 3
  d) $x^2 - x = 6$ when $y = 6$ on the graph.
  e) 3.4, −2.4
  It will not factorise

Page 151: Quadratic sequences

1 a) $4 \times 6, 5 \times 7, 6 \times 8$
  b) $4 \times 5 - 4, 5 \times 6 - 5, 6 \times 7 - 6$
  c) $4 \times 8, 5 \times 9, 6 \times 10$
2 a) 36, 49, 64
  b) n^2
  c)

1		4		9		16		25		36		49		64
	3		5		7		9		11		13		15	

  d)

64		81		100		121
	17		19		21	

3 a)

1	2	3	4	5	6
1×2	2×3	3×4	4×5	5×6	6×7

  b) $n(n+1)$
4 a) $5 \times 4 + 5, 6 \times 5 + 6, 7 \times 6 + 7$
  b) $n(n-1) + n$
  c) 1, 4, 9, 16; n^2
  d) $n^2 - n + n = n^2$

Chapter 14: Transformations

Pages 154–155: Revision Exercise

1 a) C, D, G, I   b) E, F, H
  c) (i) Translation $\binom{1}{5}$
    (ii) Reflection in $x = -3$
    (iii) Rotation, centre (−3, −3) 90° clockwise
2 Ask your teacher to check your graph.
  e) An octagon. (Note it is not quite regular)
    Mirror Symmetry in x axis, y axis, $y = x$ and $y = -x$
    Rotational symmetry about origin, order 4
3 a) Dexter has spot on right, Sinister on left
  b) Dexter: A, C, D, F, Sinister: B, E, G, H, I, J
  c) No
4 a) Enlargement, centre (0, 0), scale factor 3
  b) Enlargement, centre (0, 0), scale factor $\frac{1}{3}$
  c) Ask your teacher to check your graph.
  d) Translation $\binom{4}{0}$

Page 157: Combining transformations

1 a) (i) Reflection in y axis
    (ii) Reflection in x axis
    (iii) Rotation centre (0, 0) 180°
  b) (i) Reflection in y axis
    (ii) Reflection in $x = 1.5$
    (iii) Translation $\binom{3}{0}$
  c) (i) Yes (ii) Yes (iii) No
2 a) (i) Translation $\binom{3}{1}$
    (ii) Translation $\binom{1}{3}$
    (iii) Translation $\binom{4}{4}$
  b) (i) Yes (ii) No (iii) No
3 a) (i) Enlargement, centre (3, −2), scale factor 2
    (ii) Rotation, centre (−1, 4), 90° anticlockwise
  b) (i) Rotation, centre (0, 0), 90° anticlockwise
    (ii) Enlargement, centre (−1, −2), scale factor 2
  c) No
4 (i) $A \rightarrow C \rightarrow E$ (ii) $A \rightarrow H \rightarrow A$

Page 159: Applying transformations to graphs

1 A 3, B 1, C 2
2 c) (ii) Translation $\binom{0}{3}$
    (iii) Translation $\binom{0}{-3}$
    (iv) Reflection in x axis
3 b) Translation $\binom{0}{3}$
  c) (i) Reflection in x axis
    (ii) Reflection in $y = -1$

Chapter 15: Finance

Pages 162–163: Revision exercise

1 a) £15   b) £1125   c) £660   d) £12 585.60
2 a) £217   b) £319.80 c) £226.80
3 a) £4680   b) £17 920 c) £25 764
   d) £20 261.36   e) £2341.36
4 Tina's Taxis £13, Colin's Cabs £13.50
5 a) £564   b) £411.25 c) £8 107.50
   d) £8488.20 e) £14 365.55
6 a) 40% profit   b) 15% profit
   c) 25% loss d) 30% loss
7 a) £713   b) £42.70   c) £188.16 d) £7338.94
8 a) £16.80   b) £295.20 c) £55.20 d) 23%

Page 165: Compound interest

1 a) £66.20   b) £102.50 c) £18.54
   d) £4277.92 e) £8082.16 f) £964.88
2 a) £1770   b) £1786.52
3

Year	Amount at start of year	Interest
1	£800	£800 × 8/100 = £64
2	£864	£864 × 8/100 = £69.12
3	£933.12	£933.12 × 8/100 = £74.65
4	£1007.77	£1007.77 × 8/100 = £80.62
5	£1088.39	£1088.39 × 8/100 = £87.07

Year	Amount at end of year
1	£800 + £64 = £864
2	£864 + £69.12 = £933.12
3	£933.12 + £74.65 = £1007.77
4	£1007.77 + £80.62 = £1088.39
5	£1088.39 + £87.07 = £1175.46

4 a) £1368   b) £1361.07   c) 4 years

Page 167: Insurance

1 a) £228   b) £480   c) £408   d) £112
2 a) £27.28   b) £18.80   c) £21.78 d) £17.50
   e) Greater risk of illness/death

Page 169: Finding the original price

1 £75
2 £25 200
3 a) £852   b) £255.60
4 Lamp £80, sofa £200, Chest of drawers £102
5 a) £408   b) £340
6 £5500

Chapter 16: Perimeter, area and volume

Page 175: Perimeter and area

1 a) Perimeter = 37.7 cm, area = 113.1 cm^2
   b) Perimeter = 34 cm, area = 58 cm^2
   c) Perimeter = 44 cm, area = 69 cm^2
   d) Perimeter = 25.4 cm, area = 44.1 cm^2
2 a) Perimeter = 29.7 cm, area = 45 cm^2
   b) Perimeter = 24.2 cm, area = 25 cm^2
   c) Perimeter = 24.3 cm, area = 36 cm^2
   d) Perimeter = 30.5 cm, area = 58.5 cm^2
3 a) 1.91 m   b) 11.5 m^2

Page 177: Volume

1 a) 168 cm^3 b) 108 cm^3 c) 235.6 cm^3
   d) 296 cm^3 e) 216 cm^3 f) 57.7 cm^3
2 2.52 cm

Page 179: Using dimensions

1 (i)   a) 3 dimensions; x, x, y
         b) volume
         c) C
  (ii)   a) 1 dimension; $x + y$
         b) length
         c) A
  (iii) a) 2 dimensions; y, y
         b) area
         c) E
  (iv)   a) 2 dimensions; x, y
         b) area
         c) A
  (v)   a) 2 dimensions; $y, x + y$
         b) area
         c) D
  (vi)   a) 3 dimensions; x, x, y
         b) volume
         c) F
  (vii) a) 2 dimensions; x, y
         b) area
         c) B
  (viii) a) 1 dimension; y
         b) length
         c) E
2 a) volume
  b) area
  c) length
  d) area
  e) not a real formula
  f) area
  g) not a real formula
  h) volume

Index